# Inventions in...

# TRANSPORT

## Ian Graham

Copyright © QED Publishing 2008

First published in the UK in 2008 by
QED Publishing
A Quarto Group Company
226 City Road
London EC1V 2TT

www.qed-publishing.co.uk

A catalogue record for this book is available
from the British Library.

Printed and bound in China

ISBN  978 1 84835 091 5

**Author** Ian Graham
**Consultant** Sue Becklake
**Editor** Amanda Askew
**Designer** Gaspard de Beauvais
**Picture Researcher** Maria Joannou
**Illustrator** Richard Burgess

**Publisher** Steve Evans
**Creative Director** Zeta Davies

**Picture credits** (t=top, b=bottom, l=left, r=right)
**Alamy Images** John Henshall 24–25, Guichaoua 13b
**Corbis** 12t, Jean Becker/Sygma 3t, 22b, Bettmann 6t, 24b, 28l,
Car Culture 8b, 8–9, Hulton-Deutsch Collection 10t,
Michael Macor/San Francisco Chronicle 7t, Carl & Ann Purcell 17t,
Reuters 16b, Eberhard Streichan/Zefa 14–15, Tim de Waele 10–11
**Department of Defence** 18b
**DK Images** 4t
**Getty Images** AFP Photo/Jamal Nasrallah-Files 6–7, AFP Photo/
Yoshikazu Tsuno 11t, Koichi Kamoshida 15t, Time Life Pictures/
Mansell 23t
**Hawkes Ocean Technologies** 21b
**Istockphoto** 11b
**NASA** 26t, 26–27, 28–29, 29b
**Scaled Composites** 26b
**Science Photo Library** Mike Agliolo 20-21
**Shutterstock** 3, 4–5, 5t, 12–13, 13t, 22–23, 25t
**US Navy** 16-17, 18-19, 19t, 21t
**Virgin Trains** 12b

Words in **bold** can be found in
the glossary on page 30.

# Contents

# INVENTIONS IN TRANSPORT

Hundreds of inventions have made transport faster, easier and safer. Some of these inventions were made by scientists and engineers working for big companies, but many of them were made by ordinary people with a bright idea.

## On land

The wheel is probably the most important transport invention ever. With the wheel, it was possible to build horse-drawn carts and carriages. Later, the invention of **engines** led to the first vehicles that could move by themselves without having to be pulled by animals.

The wheel was probably invented in Mesopotamia about 5500 years ago to use with carts and chariots.

The largest ships today are as big as a skyscraper lying on its side.

## In and on the water

For thousands of years, sea voyages relied on oar power or wind and sails – until the steam engine was invented. **Steamships** could sail even if there was no wind. Since then, inventors have found lots of new ways to travel in water.

# INVENTIONS IN TRANSPORT

| 3500 BCE | Wheel |
|---|---|
| 1620s AD | Submarine |
| 1769 | Steam-powered vehicle |
| 1804 | Steam locomotive |
| 1852 | Airship |
| 1885 | Car |
| 1885 | Motorbike |
| 1903 | Aeroplane |
| 1907 | Helicopter |
| 1949 | Jet airliner |
| 1955 | Hovercraft |
| 1961 | Manned spacecraft |
| 1964 | High-speed electric train |
| 1973 | Jet Ski |
| 1981 | Space shuttle |

## In the air

The invention of the aeroplane and then the jet airliner allowed people to travel further and faster than ever before. The **jet engine** was invented by Englishman Frank Whittle and German Hans von Ohain in the 1930s. It once took about four months to travel to the other side of the world by sailing ship. Now flying there takes less than 24 hours. A few lucky people can even soar away into space and circle the whole world every 90 minutes.

Two billion people fly in an airliner every year. All but the smallest airliners are powered by jet engines.

# KING OF THE ROAD

**The invention of the car changed our everyday lives. Today, there are about 750 million cars on the roads.**

Benz's 1885 car had a top speed of less than 15 kilometres an hour.

## *Steam power*

In 1769, Frenchman Nicolas-Joseph Cugnot put a small **steam engine** on a cart and made the first vehicle that could move using its own **power**. It could only go at walking speed, but it showed that a cart could move on its own. Other inventors then began to make better and faster vehicles.

## *The first car*

The car was invented in 1885 by German engineer Karl Benz. It had three wheels and was powered by a small **petrol** engine at the back.

## DID YOU KNOW?

**Inventors are still coming up with new ideas for cars. Some cars can take off and fly like planes. The first flying car was the Autoplane, designed by American Glenn Curtiss in 1917, but it never took off. The first car to fly was the Aerobile, built by American inventor Waldo Waterman in 1937.**

The flying Moller Skycar will be able to reach a top speed of 600 kilometres an hour!

## Supersonic *speed*

Jet cars are powered by jet engines. They were invented in the 1960s to set speed records. A car called Thrust SSC is the fastest jet car in the world. In 1997, it went 1228 kilometres an hour – faster than the speed of sound! It could have driven across the USA from New York to Los Angeles, a distance of 4500 kilometres, in about 3.5 hours. It would take about two days at normal road speeds.

Two jet engines make Thrust SSC as powerful as 145 racing cars!

# INTO THE FUTURE

**Nearly all cars today have engines that burn petrol fuel. Car makers are trying out new types of car engine and new fuels for the future.**

## After oil

Engines that burn petrol give out harmful gases, so some car makers are testing cleaner engines. New engines and fuels will be needed anyway because the oil that petrol is made from will run out one day.

CleanEnergy
Powered by Hydrogen

The Nissan Pivo is a future car powered by **electric motors** inside its wheels.

PIVO²

## Electric cars

Cars can be powered by electric motors. The electric carriage was invented in the 1830s, but cars with petrol engines became more popular. Now, people are interested in electric cars again because they do not burn fuel and so do not give out any harmful gases.

## Hydrogen *power*

The hydrogen-powered car was invented in the 1860s, but became more widely developed in the 1970s. It uses hydrogen gas instead of petrol. When hydrogen burns, it produces water instead of fumes. The Ford Fusion Hydrogen 999 is a car powered by hydrogen fuel cells. It can reach a speed of 330 kilometres an hour.

## DID YOU KNOW?

In the 1890s, the fastest cars in the world were electric. In 1899, they reached a speed of 105 kilometres an hour and people were amazed. They thought a driver would die if he went that fast!

The BMW H2R is a hydrogen-powered racing car that can reach a top speed of 300 kilometres an hour.

# ON TWO WHEELS

**Bikes have been around for about 200 years. They have changed a lot in that time and new two-wheelers are still being developed today.**

A solid back wheel and a lightweight frame lets a racing bike slip through the air faster than an ordinary bike.

### *Pushing pedals*

Scotsman Kirkpatrick Macmillan made the first bike with pedals in 1842, but the pedals went forwards and backwards! The modern bicycle was invented by English inventor John Kemp Starley in 1885. His invention was the Rover safety bicycle. It had a diamond-shaped frame, equal-sized wheels and a chain turning the back wheel.

High-wheeler or penny-farthing bikes were popular in the 1870s. The rider sat on top of the front wheel.

### DID YOU KNOW?

**Tyres filled with air, called** pneumatic **tyres, were invented by Scotsman Robert Thomson in 1845, but they were impractical. Then in 1888, Scotsman John Boyd Dunlop made better pneumatic tyres. Dunlop's tyres were a great success.**

## Motorbikes

The first motorbike was built in 1885 by two German engineers, Gottlieb Daimler and Wilhelm Maybach. On 10 November 1885, Daimler's son rode it and became the world's first motorcyclist.

The future Yamaha Gen-Ryu motorbike has a petrol engine and an electric motor.

## Lean and go

One of the most advanced two-wheelers is the Segway. It was invented by American Dean Kamen in 2001. The rider stands on a platform and holds onto the handle. Electric motors turn the wheels. Whichever way you lean, that is the way it goes.

The Segway is easy to ride because it balances by itself.

# ON THE TRACKS

Trains were invented in the early 1800s. They were steam powered. Today, high-speed electric trains whisk passengers from city to city as fast as racing cars. Japan's bullet train was the first high-speed train.

The first railway line across the USA was built in 1869.

## Steam power

The steam **locomotive**, the engine that pulls a train, was invented by Richard Trevithick in Britain in 1804. The first locomotives were used in mines and ironworks to move heavy wagons of coal and iron.

Tilting passenger trains, such as the Pendolino, are used in several European countries.

## Tilting trains

Passenger trains can go round bends faster if they tilt. Tilting stops things sliding off the tables. The first tilting trains were built in Spain in the 1950s.

Japan's 500 series bullet train is one of the fastest passenger trains in the world. It has a top speed of 300 kilometres an hour.

## Bullet trains

The first high-speed train, named the bullet train, was invented in Japan in 1964. New railway lines were built specially for the trains so that they could go as fast as possible. Since they started running, they have carried about six billion passengers.

## DID YOU KNOW?

**The TGV set a passenger train speed record of 574 kilometres an hour in 2007 – nearly twice as fast as a racing car.**

## TGV

France's high-speed train service is called Train à Grande Vitesse or TGV, meaning high-speed train. It started running in 1981. It worked so well that similar high-speed trains were built in other countries, such as the USA, Spain and South Korea.

High-speed trains, such as the TGV, are sleek and **streamlined** so that they can slip through the air as fast as possible.

# FLYING TRAINS

**The most advanced trains float above the track.** Magnets **lift the trains into the air and fly them along the rails.**

## Magnetic marvels

Flying trains are called **maglevs**. People started thinking about using magnets to make a train float in the air in the early 1900s. Work started on the first maglevs in the 1960s, mainly in Japan and Germany.

Transrapid    Europa

Maglevs in Germany are tested on this special track.

## DID YOU KNOW?

The first high-speed maglev railway opened in China in 2002. It carries passengers between the city of Shanghai and its airport.

## Low-flying trains

The first maglev was opened to the public in Birmingham, England. From 1984 to 1995, it carried passengers between the city's airport and railway station. The trains were **automatic** – there were no drivers. They travelled at a speed of 42 kilometres an hour.

>>

In 2003, a Japanese maglev set the world record speed of 581 kilometres an hour.

## Super fliers

The fastest maglevs can travel at a greater speed than other trains because they do not touch the track. They cannot go on ordinary railway lines. Special tracks called guideways are built.

Magnets in the train and track raise the train above the track.

>>

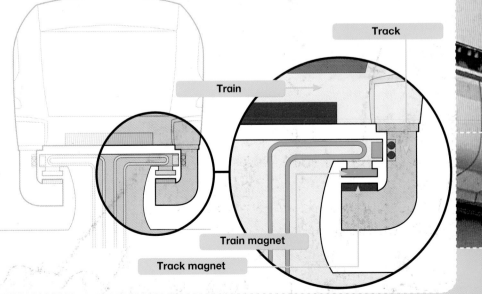

Track

Train

Train magnet

Track magnet

# ON THE WATER

**Boats can go faster if they fly above the surface of the water instead of travelling through it.**

> The invention of the sailing ship led to great voyages of discovery.

### *First boats*

Boats have been used as transport for thousands of years. The ancient Egyptians travelled along the Nile River by boat, and many people built ships for war.

When a hydrofoil rises up out of the water, it is not bumped about by the waves and so it gives passengers a smoother ride.

## Hydrofoil

One way to make a boat travel above water is to use wings. They work like a plane's wings, but underwater. When the hydrofoil speeds up, the underwater wings lift it out of the water. When it slows down, the boat sits in the water again.

## Hovercraft

In the 1950s, English engineer and inventor Christopher Cockerell built a new type of vehicle – a hovercraft. Air is blown down underneath a hovercraft, pushing it up above the water. A hovercraft can skim over land just as easily as water – so it can go places that a boat cannot.

The US Navy uses hovercraft to bring soldiers and equipment ashore from ships.

## DID YOU KNOW?

In 1965, American Clayton Jacobson II invented the Sea-Doo. It scooted across the water like a floating motorbike. It was not a success. When the Jet Ski was introduced in 1973, it was a big hit.

# FULL STEAM AHEAD

**Steam power seems old-fashioned today, but the most advanced warships and submarines still rely on steam. Their engines are nuclear-powered steam engines.**

## Nuclear fuel

Most ships have engines that burn a fuel such as petrol or oil. A nuclear-powered ship or submarine is different. Its **nuclear fuel**, uranium, gets very hot on its own and it stays hot for years. The heat boils water, which changes into steam. The steam drives generators that make electricity and also turns the **propellers**.

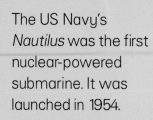

The US Navy's *Nautilus* was the first nuclear-powered submarine. It was launched in 1954.

## Nuclear vessels

The first nuclear-powered vessels were built in the 1950s. With nuclear power, a submarine can stay hidden underwater for several months. Nuclear-powered warships can go anywhere in the world's oceans without having to keep stopping for fuel.

## Catapults on ships

Ships called **aircraft carriers** use steam in another way. Planes take off from an aircraft carrier's deck. A plane has to be going fast enough to take off when it gets to the end of the deck or it will fall into the sea. To give it some extra speed, a huge catapult powered by steam hurls the plane along the deck. The idea to use steam in this way came from Commander Colin Mitchell of the British Royal Navy in 1950.

A steam catapult sends a fighter flying off the deck of an aircraft carrier.

The US Navy's giant *Nimitz* aircraft carrier has four propellers driven by steam from two **nuclear reactors**.

## DID YOU KNOW?

**A *Nimitz* warship has eight steam-powered generators producing enough electricity for a small city.**

# GOING UNDER

**Inventors started trying to build submarines 400 years ago. Today, giant submarines cruise the oceans and tiny diving craft called** submersibles **explore the seabed.**

## First submarines

The first person to design a submarine was Englishman William Bourne in 1578, but he did not build it. Dutchman Cornelis Drebbel built the first submarine in the 1620s. It was a wooden boat covered with greased leather to stop water getting in. Twelve oarsmen rowed it underwater in the River Thames in London, England.

Submarines dive by letting seawater flood into tanks to make them heavier.

## Modern subs

The modern submarine was developed by Irish-American John P Holland. A submarine he built in 1897 was bought by the US Navy. Other navies soon bought their own submarines. Submarines were widely used during World War I (1914–1918) and World War II (1939–1945). The German navy's submarines were known as U-boats.

## DID YOU KNOW?

**The first military submarine was called the *Turtle*. It was built in 1775 by American David Bushnell. Letting some water inside made it heavier, so that it sank lower. To come up again, the water was pumped out with a hand pump. Turning a propeller by hand moved it slowly through the water.**

Seat

Pump

Propeller

The *Turtle* tried to blow up British warship HMS *Eagle* in 1776, but it failed.

## Flying underwater

In the 1990s, Englishman Graham Hawkes invented a new submersible with wings. *Deep Flight 1* works like an underwater plane 'flying' through the water.

DF 1001-X

*Deep Flight 1* can dive up to 1000 metres.

# TAKE-OFF

**The first flights were made by people in balloons, but balloons floated wherever the wind blew them. Inventors soon started looking for ways of making flying machines that they could steer.**

## Hot-air balloons

Hot air is lighter than cold air. Smoke rises from a fire because hot air floats upwards and carries the smoke up with it. In 1783, two French brothers, Joseph and Étienne Montgolfier, filled a big balloon with hot air and watched it rise up over Paris with two brave passengers. It was the first manned flight.

In 1999, *Breitling Orbiter 3* made the first balloon flight around the world without landing.

## *The Wright brothers*

Orville and Wilbur Wright were bicycle makers from Dayton, Ohio, USA. In the early 1900s, they built **gliders** and flew them. Then in 1903, they built an aircraft with an engine. On 17 December 1903, Orville used it to make the first aeroplane flight at Kitty Hawk, North Carolina, USA.

The Wright brothers' aeroplane, Flyer, took off for the first ever powered flight in 1903.

## *Modern aircraft*

Aircraft today are marvels of engineering. Their designers make use of the latest inventions in materials, engines, electronics and computers to produce the best possible aircraft. The European plane maker, Airbus, produced nearly 400 inventions of its own for the new A380 airliner.

The biggest airliner in the world is the Airbus A380. Each of its giant wings is about 40 metres in length.

## DID YOU KNOW?

The first flight of the Wright Flyer only lasted for 12 seconds. It flew 36 metres at an average speed of 12 kilometres an hour. Longer flights soon followed.

# SPINNING BLADES

**Helicopters can take off straight up in the air and hover in one place. They can fly like this because they have spinning blades.**

## *The first helicopter*

The first person to take off and fly using spinning blades was Frenchman Paul Cornu in 1907. He only just managed to get off the ground for a few seconds. It was another 30 years before helicopters could stay in the air for an hour.

WORLDS RECORD
BROKEN
1 HOUR 20 MIN

A year after its first short flight in 1940, Sikorsky's helicopter set a new world record by staying in the air for more than 90 minutes.

## Helicopters today

The modern helicopter was developed by Russian-American Igor Sikorsky in 1940. His helicopter had a big set of blades at the top and a small set at the end of its tail. Helicopters are still built like this today.

A helicopter's ability to hover and to land vertically makes it ideal for search and rescue work and police air patrols.

The Osprey is a tiltrotor. It takes off like a helicopter, then its engines tilt down and it flies like a plane.

## Tiltrotors

Tiltrotors are planes with swivelling engines. With the engines tilted up, the propellers work like helicopter blades and lift the plane straight up. The tiltrotor was invented in the USA in 1954.

## DID YOU KNOW?

Igor Sikorsky was born in Kiev, Ukraine, in 1889. He built the first plane with four engines in 1913. He moved to the USA in 1919 and built passenger planes. Then he built the first successful helicopter. He died in 1972.

# INTO SPACE

Until the 1960s, the idea of travelling into space was just a dream. Since then, more than 460 people from 34 countries have gone into space.

Early manned **spacecraft**, such as the American Mercury capsules, were tiny – just big enough for one person to fit inside.

## First into space

The first manned spacecraft, *Vostok 1*, was launched in 1961. Russian pilot Yuri Gagarin sat inside the tiny ball-shaped craft. He flew around the world once and landed. The whole flight took 108 minutes.

*SpaceShipOne* won a prize of $10 million by flying into space in 2004. It was the first manned spacecraft launched by a private company, not a space agency, such as NASA.

## Spaceplanes

Early manned spacecraft could only be used once. Then in 1981, the US space agency, NASA, launched a new type of manned spacecraft called the **space shuttle**. It can be used many times.

## Soyuz spacecraft

Russia's manned spacecraft is called Soyuz. It made its first manned flight in 1967. Today, the latest type of Soyuz spacecraft carries **astronauts** to the **International Space Station** and brings them back to Earth again.

A Soyuz spacecraft carries a **crew** of three astronauts.

## DID YOU KNOW?

*Vostok 1* launched the first man into space. *Vostok 2* was the first manned spacecraft to spend more than one day in space. *Vostok 6* launched the first woman into space.

# ROCKETS AND SHUTTLES

**Spaceflight depends on** rockets **because they are the only vehicles powerful enough to launch spacecraft.**

Robert Goddard's rocket only rose to a height of 12 metres, but it showed that liquid-fuel rockets could work.

## *Rockets*

Spacecraft, such as the American space shuttle and Russian Soyuz, are launched by rockets. Rockets that burn solid fuel were invented in China about 1000 years ago. Most big space rockets burn liquid fuel. This type of rocket was invented by American scientist Robert Goddard in 1926. He launched a small rocket from his aunt's farm in Auburn, Massachusetts, USA.

Two giant, solid-fuel rocket boosters supply most of the power needed to lift the space shuttle off its launch pad.

## Space shuttle

The space shuttle has three parts – the Orbiter, the external tank and the solid-fuel rocket boosters. The Orbiter is the spaceplane the crew travels in. The external tank holds fuel for three rocket engines in the Orbiter's tail. The boosters add more power. The tank and boosters fall back to Earth, while the Orbiter flies on into space.

### DID YOU KNOW?

At the end of a mission, the space shuttle Orbiter re-enters the Earth's atmosphere at 25 times the speed of sound.

The space shuttle usually carries a crew of up to seven astronauts.

*Catherine had a cold there for about two weeks and she was very bad. We nearly got the doctor out, but I treated her with an ounce of liquorice stick steeped in water and it seemed to help. The damp weather is a curse. We have been keeping the fire going all night. It is the season for it, I think. At Mass everyone is coughing.*

*The little ones are doing well too. They are getting big and bold. I'm in the middle of finishing off two jumpers I pulled together from some extra wool I had. My eyesight is not great any more though, so I don't spend too long at it in the evenings.*

*Has the food improved any? And what about the lice? I hate to think of you scratching in there. If you want, I will see if I can send in some lotion. I am sure I could get something for you in the chemist's. Just let me know and I will ask.*

*I'm including matches and papers like you asked. Next time I will send tobacco if you need it.*

*There hasn't been much news. There was a house fire up the road. Mr. and Mrs. McEvoy's place. The whole roof went up. The walls are left but they are very black, and I don't think it is safe. They were lucky not to be killed. They are staying with her sister. I think it was a spark that did it, which is unusual in the winter months, but there you go.*

*I haven't had any letters from the rest of the family except from Winnie, though she barely has any time to write. Her poor mistress passed away. Mrs. Thomas, a lovely blonde woman. She died straight after her baby was born. So Winnie is up the walls looking after the baby and the house and*

Mr. Thomas is in a bad way. They are looking for a nanny and putting an advert in the Drogheda Conservative this week. I hope they get someone good, so Winnie can get a bit of a break.

Christmas is coming and we are getting ready to whitewash. We're looking to choose a goose too and I have my eye on a nice fat one down the yard. He runs away from me every time I go out to feed them, so I think he knows.

It is not very nice to be where you are for Christmas, but I suppose it is nice knowing it will be your last Christmas in there. I'd say you are counting down the weeks.

That's all from Kells. All is well. Write soon and let me know as always if there is anything you need.

Your loving sister,

Susan

*❧*

*The Advertisement*

**Drogheda Conservative, January 1880**
# WANTED

**A Respectable Woman to Take Charge
of a Motherless Child
Three Weeks Old
To Bottle-feed it
Liberal Terms Will Be Given
Apply to W.D. Thomas
43 Laurence Street, Drogheda**

# CHAPTER 2

## *The Nanny*

The train arrived on time, a black-grey plume of smoke following it through the station. The smoke separated in wisps, floating up towards the yellow ironworks ceiling, before the wind caught it and pushed it out along the track, where it disappeared into the skyline.

She descended the steps of the train and stood, looking left, towards the station door. Her back was straight, almost wooden, and her small bustle drew the eye to the curve of her behind. Her hair was fashioned neatly, a small hat attached to the side of her head with a pin. In one hand she carried a brown case.

A flurry of activity surrounded the open goods carriages, with men in flat caps lifting boxes from the train onto

7

trolleys on the platform, while porters removed luggage from the passenger carriages.

As the smoke cleared, she made her way to the turnstile and gave the stationmaster a thin-lipped smile.

A row of vehicles were lined up at the door, a mix of family carriages, farm carts and traps. It was January and the horses blew sharp white breaths into the cold air. The drivers had scarves wrapped around their faces and necks, tweed caps pulled close to their eyebrows.

She walked by the waiting traps and cabs, taking small prim steps down the hill, out of the station grounds and onto the Dublin Road. Dark ice filled the puddles tipping the edges of the footpath.

She could hear birdsong as she quickened her pace. She had allowed plenty of time, but she couldn't quite remember the distance.

Delivery carts rolled up the hill, the squat muscular ponies straining to carry the loads, bringing milk, groceries and coal. On her left loomed a giant grey building, surrounded by a tall stone wall. Black iron bars were on every window. She kept her head high and did not look across at the small sign on a wooden plaque, nailed to the stone gatepost.

*Drogheda Union Workhouse*

She lifted her boots to get her past the tall stone wall faster. When she was far enough away, she released the breath she hadn't been aware she was holding and allowed herself to look out over the town, her vantage point allowing a sight of church spires, red fancy brickwork, grey stone factories with chimneys billowing smoke.

A wide, brown river cut through the centre of the town, curving and hiding itself from view ahead. Standing majestically over the town was the Viaduct bridge, its crisscross iron railings planted on top of giant arches, holding up the trains as they passed on their way north.

At the bottom of James' Street she came to the Bullring, a small square area where hardware shops had their goods set out. Women in country clothes stood beside pipes and brushes, grates and shovels, chatting.

She felt some eyes on her as she walked past, the chatter stopping for a moment. She doubted anyone would remember her. She looked back at the women watching her and they burst into conversation again, turning their heads sharply to look away.

She crossed the bridge over the River Boyne to Shop Street, where attractive stores advertised clothing and fancy goods. She passed by the Augustinian church, set behind black railings, back from the road. She took the right at the top of Shop Street and there before her stood Laurence Street, a bend in the middle, sweeping into the distance.

Slowly, she counted the numbers, looking at each door as she passed.

She walked by a house painted pale blue and came back to read the black iron numbers on the door: 43.

She was early. The door was grimy. Two low windows were set in the façade, white windowsills turned grey. It wasn't the most attractive house. She could see up ahead that there much finer buildings, with railings and steps and basements. Her gloved finger lingered on the button doorbell. Changing her mind, she lifted the large knocker, knocked three times and stood back.

No answer. She waited for another few moments. Impatiently, she tapped her boot on the pavement, curling her lip slightly, thinking. She lifted the knocker again and was about to try another rap when she saw the curtain twitching at the front.

Within seconds, the front door swung open, a frazzled woman holding it, hissing, "*You've wakened her! Can't you read?*"

She pointed to a small white card pinned below the knocker, printed in capitals, emphasising the commands.

NO VISITORS. NO DOORBELL. KNOCK GENTLY.

"I'm here about the advertisement. About the baby."

"Oh," said the woman, her face softening. "Oh, of course. Come in."

She crossed the limestone step and stood in the hallway. It was tiled in tiny small squares, a patterned mosaic in beiges and browns. The woman led her into the front room where the white net curtains blocked the light from the street.

"I'm Mrs. McHugh, the housekeeper," she said. "Please, take a seat."

The room had a high ceiling and two low Queen Anne velvet couches. She sat down, perching her behind on the edge of the couch, looking round her when the woman left the room. Two vases of decaying flowers stood on the hearth. Their scent filled the room, an acrid smell. A cabinet filled with china and ornaments was placed near the door, the surface covered in dust. In the corner near the fireplace was a small writing bureau, in the same colour wood as the cabinet. Its lid was open, papers stuffed in the pockets, newspapers, pens, ink and string piled up in a mess. Everything needed a good clean. She expected there hadn't been time.

Minutes passed. She kept her posture, not allowing herself to sag. She could hear movement upstairs, but still no one came to attend to her.

A cry rang out. A newborn cry. It hung in the air, sharp, painful.

After some time, she got up from the couch and walked around, her heeled boots digging into the light-blue wool rug. It was pretty, a soft pink rose woven into it. Black streaks nestled in the fibres.

The door opened behind her and she turned to find a man standing there. He was tall, his face thin, his shock of black hair wetted and smoothed on his head. He looked dishevelled and tired.

"Good morning," he said, his voice low. He had a large black moustache, a small gap between it and his sideburns. "I'm sorry for the wait. Do sit down."

She returned to her seat and perched gently, leaning forward, keeping her chin up.

"I'm sorry for your loss," she said.

He sat down, pulling his trousers up slightly to allow his long legs to bend.

"Yes," he said. "A terrible loss." He paused, no emotion showing on his face.

"Can you tell me about yourself ... Miss ...?"

"Miss Murphy," she said. "Margaret Murphy. Well, I'm from Dublin. The southside. Rathmines. I worked as a governess for the past three years. They're gone to boarding school now. Lovely girls. I was sad to leave. Before that I was with another family in Dublin. And before that I worked in Wicklow."

"And babies?" said Mr. Thomas. "What experience do you have with babies?"

"Oh, I adore babies," she said. "My family in Wicklow had a wee one who I was very attached to. The baby is three weeks old, sir?"

"Four," he said. "She's four weeks now."

"And how is she doing?"

11

He paused. "Not very well, to be honest," he said. "She is crying. Hunger, I think. Mrs. McHugh tries her best, but she cries day and night."

"Ah," she said. "That can happen with the bottle, you know."

"Can it?" he said.

"I have a lot of experience with bottle-feeding. My family in Wicklow decided on the same thing, not to go with a wet nurse, so I am well used to making up bottles. It causes extra wind in the child, you see, so you need to give gripe water, something to ease the poor little mite. Yes, I have plenty of experience with that."

He looked relieved. "Well, that's good then. And references, have you brought any?"

She picked up her case and put it on the couch, clicking open the locks. She sifted through the papers inside and produced her references, one stamped with a wax seal.

She rose and handed them to him.

"Yes," he said quietly to himself as he studied them. "Very good."

From upstairs the muffled cries of the baby could be heard.

"I'd like you to meet her," he said. "Could you come this way?"

He opened the door, allowing her to pass first, then he climbed the stairwell, holding on to the banister, his footsteps heavy. The cries grew louder as they climbed. He took her to the first floor and into the child's bedroom. Balled-up sheets were strewn about. A dressing table was covered in glass bottles, some empty, some half full. Powdered milk was scattered in spilled piles, large rubber teats sitting among the mess.

A low wooden cradle was centred on the floor.

Behind it stood Mrs. McHugh, her hair sticking out in wisps around her face. She clutched the wailing baby to her, shushing her, trying to rock the cries from her.

"Let me try," the woman said, walking across the room, peeling the gloves from her hands.

She took the crying infant and the blanket from Mrs. McHugh. The baby was red in the face and was shuddering. She wrapped the blanket tightly around the child, swaddling her, and held her close to her chest.

She held her hand out for the bottle.

"It's too cold," she said. "Do you have a jug of hot water, to put it in?"

Mrs. McHugh looked at Mr. Thomas and said, "I'll get one."

The woman squeezed the baby tight, pushing her into her breast, humming a low sound.

"Sometimes she takes the milk, sometimes she doesn't," said Mr. Thomas, his hand gesturing to the table of baby food.

"I find sugar helps," she said. "But the milk must be kept warm, don't allow it to go cold."

Wrapped tight, the baby began to calm a bit, her heavy cries becoming light, peppered with hiccups now. Mrs. McHugh returned with a jug of hot water. The woman held the baby as the bottle warmed in the jug, then tested the milk on the inside of her wrist before using her fingers to rub the milk along the child's gums and lips.

The baby thrust her mouth open and took the rubber teat offered. She drank, her jaws working as she suckled the milk hungrily.

Mr. Thomas and Mrs. McHugh stood and watched the woman sit down in the rocking chair in the corner. She fed the baby, while rocking gently back and forth.

When the child had finished half the bottle, she placed her along her arm as though she were petting a cat and patted her back.

"A cloth, please," she said.

Mrs. McHugh promptly produced a muslin.

She winded the baby, fed her the rest of the bottle and winded her once more. Full of milk, the child's eyes fell backwards a little. She lifted her and placed her in the crib, covering her with a white crocheted blanket. The baby turned her head and went to sleep, her tiny chest rising up and down with her breaths.

Silently, the three left the bedroom and stood on the landing.

"I would like to have a word with Mrs. McHugh," Mr. Thomas said. "Could I trouble you to wait in the sitting room, Miss Murphy?"

"Of course," she said, and walked down the stairs, a smile, unseen, planted on her lips.

She waited, sitting, satisfied, her hands curled in her lap.

Things had gone well. The baby had cooperated. She knew she would be taken on now.

The door opened and Mr. Thomas appeared, his face less strained than when he had first presented himself.

He smiled and held out his arms in a welcoming gesture.

"When would you be in a position to start?"

# CHAPTER 3

## Mrs. McHugh

The nights and days had merged into one. Tears. Towellings. Dinners. Turning away visitors. And, all the time, the child had cried. A single bed had been moved into the baby's room and she had lain there, passed out with exhaustion until the child's cries pierced her black dreams again. And the grief. The grief she felt for Mrs. Thomas. Who would never see her baby grow up. Who would never feel the suckle of her child.

Sometimes, when it had got too much, she had cried into her sleeve – hot angry tears – for Mr. Thomas, for the baby girl, for herself who had lost a friend in Mrs. Thomas, a confidante. But the tears didn't help. And they wouldn't help raise the child either.

There was only one maidservant now at Number 43. Ethel did most of the heavy housework and the errands. She also helped in the kitchen, chopping, preparing, baking. Mrs. McHugh prided herself on being an efficient housekeeper, ordering the groceries, planning the meals and ensuring the girl cleaned like she was supposed to. They sent their laundry out and organised most of the household decorations and crafts themselves.

Mrs. Thomas had a talent for flower arranging and the last vase arrangements she'd made were still in the sitting room. She had yet to find the courage to throw them out. They stood, turning brown, dripping their crispy, soiled leaves onto the mantelpiece. She had changed the water, pouring the green slimy liquid down the sink and replacing it with fresh, but she had put the wilted flowers back, hoping to get more time out of them. She should have organised to press them, to dry them out between the thick books from the dining room cabinet, but it was too late now.

All of the staff rooms under the attic lay empty. A collection of clutter had been added slowly, year on year, to the dark airless attic.

On the floor beneath the old servant rooms was Mr. and Mrs. Thomas's bedroom, a spacious room that took up the width of the house. It offered a wide view of the street below through two large sash windows.

Below the master bedroom was the nursery and two guest bedrooms. The bedrooms were small and dark, but Mrs. McHugh kept them aired and changed the linen as regularly as she could to prevent the damp.

Many times, as Mrs. McHugh had sat in the nursery, clutching the crying child to her, going over in her mind all the tasks that remained undone in the house, she'd thought of the servant rooms and their vacantness, of the quiet stairs where once many footsteps had trod. She longed now for those extra hands.

For a cook who could prepare meals and hot food for Mr. Thomas who seemed to be fading before her eyes. For another two maidservants who could wash and clean and help with the soiled baby clothes that never seemed to cease. And for an errand boy, who could fetch the various new paraphernalia they needed for the baby. They hadn't expected to be bottle-feeding her.

At least now, with the arrival of the Nanny, one of the servant rooms would be occupied. And she herself would be able to go home to sleep beside her husband. Mick had been so patient and understanding these past weeks.

She wasn't quite sure what to make of Miss Murphy on first appearance. She seemed a bit stiff, proper. And she didn't like the way she'd ordered her about, demanding hot water and towels – she didn't like that at all. But she had settled the baby and, for that, Mrs. McHugh was grateful. If she could take over the management of the child, her feeds, her comfort, her care, at least she herself could get back to running the house. She could help Mr. Thomas get back to some semblance of his life.

"You can see everything from here," she said.

She stood with the Nanny in the guest bedroom to the front of the house. It was the nicer guest bedroom, with light wallpaper and a reaching view onto the street below.

The Nanny was looking out the window, separating the net curtain with her fingers.

"You must have been very fond of her," she said, her eyes fixed on the street.

17

"Mrs. Thomas?" asked Mrs. McHugh. "Yes," she said softly. "Very."

The Nanny continued to stare, until Mrs. McHugh folded her arms and coughed impatiently.

"Yes, this will do nicely," the Nanny said, pulling herself away from the window and looking around the bedroom.

"I'm sure Mr. Thomas will decide on a more permanent arrangement," said Mrs. McHugh. "We'll sort out the attic rooms – they need to be cleared out and aired. They're not bad for attic rooms though."

"Oh, this room is perfectly adequate," said the Nanny.

"But this is a guest bedroom."

"Yes, and it's fine."

"We have staff quarters," said Mrs. McHugh.

"I'll need to be near the baby," said the Nanny.

Mrs. McHugh pursed her lips. She walked over to the washstand and hung a towel onto the rail.

"I'll leave you to get settled, Miss Murphy. You are very welcome to Number 43. It is a very lovely house and Mr. Thomas is a nice and accommodating employer. I do hope we will work well together."

The Nanny glared at her before nodding her head slightly. Mrs. McHugh wasn't sure if it was in agreement or defiance.

For the rest of the day, the Nanny cared for the baby, calling Mrs. McHugh to the room several times to discuss her feed, the preparation of formula, the method of washing bottles. "We can't be too careful," she said.

Mrs. McHugh felt a bit put out that her sanitary habits were being questioned, when it came to the baby. She had spent every waking moment looking after the child since she was born. She had done nothing but her best for her.

In the evening, Mrs. McHugh prepared a meal of boiled ham and cabbage for Mr. Thomas.

"Mrs. McHugh, will you ask Miss Murphy if she'd like to join me?" he said.

She looked at him in surprise.

"That is if the baby is asleep," he said.

The house echoed in silence, the chaos of the past month eerily quietened. It seemed the baby was indeed asleep.

Mrs. McHugh wiped her hands on her apron and climbed the stairs towards the nursery. She opened the door quietly and found the Nanny standing over the cot, her arms outstretched into it. She jumped slightly as Mrs. McHugh came into the room.

"She's quiet for you?" asked the housekeeper.

"She's calmed right down."

"Mr. Thomas would like you to have dinner with him. It's ready now."

The Nanny backed away from the cot and followed Mrs. McHugh onto the landing and down the stairs.

At the table, the housekeeper poured the two diners water to drink. Mr. Thomas asked for wine to be brought to the table.

"To celebrate Miss Murphy's first day," he said. "And a sleeping baby." A smile crossed his face.

It was the first time Mrs. McHugh had seen a smile pass his lips in a month.

She poured the wine, careful to not overfill Miss Murphy's glass.

"If that is all for tonight, sir, I think I will be on my way," Mrs. McHugh said.

"Yes, of course, Mrs. McHugh. Thank you."

She bowed her head a little and walked away from the table, smoothing her apron.

"Oh, Mrs. McHugh!" he called just as she left the room.

"Yes," she answered, retracing her steps a little.

"The guest bedroom. I don't see why Miss Murphy can't remain there for the moment. It's near the baby. It will suit fine."

"Yes, Mr. Thomas," she said, looking at the Nanny who had her head bowed, on her mouth a trace of a tight-lipped smile.

# CHAPTER 4

*Betty*

You see all sorts from up here. Fights. Kisses. Children breaking from their mother's hands and darting right across the road, nearly under the legs of a horse. They're so innocent, those kids. With their white faces looking out from their bonnets, their little hands gripping onto their mothers' tightly, until they spy something more interesting that they must dash to.

I look out on the street all day. I pause between my reading and taking my meals to overlook the goings-on right under my window, under my nose. I see a lot from up here. Secrets. I know that Mr. Ferriter, the butcher across the road, takes in meat that's not fresh, that has already done the rounds in the shops in Dublin, and he chittles it down and sells it for cheap here. I tell the girl not to buy any scrap of carcass from him at all, and if I catch any of his fibrous offal floating in my soup, she'll be for the sack.

I know that Mrs. Shepherd has a thing for Mr. Ferriter and she leans across the counter and touches his arm when he's slicing up the meat for her. I see her, laughing, throwing her head back, flirting. I hear things too. Boys with the handcarts, shouting. The brewery deliveries and the barrels as they clunk and roll into the cellar. Horses' hooves clopping by all day and, at the weekends, the bustle of the fancy carriages making their way to the Whitworth at the top of the road for the dances and opera performances and shows. What I'd give to be able to see a show now!

I hear the girl, coming in the morning, always late, flying in, nearly bursting the door off the hinges. She thinks I don't notice she's late, but I notice everything. I've added up the five minutes here and the ten minutes there and I reckon she owes me at least a month in overtime by now. But I say nothing, because I don't trust that she wouldn't spit in my tripe and I know some of her family from the far side are as rough as they come.

There's no harm to her, but she's thicker than I like in a girl. I'd love her to pick up one of my books, to feel the jacket, to ask what it's about and if she could borrow it. That would be my ideal type of girl. That type of girl could have been my daughter.

My favourite days are Fridays. Those were always my favourite days in the shop – the busiest days, when the wages came in and the form was merry and the tick would be paid off a bit and you'd have groceries going out up to your ears and the men coming into the pub for pints. There was always something about Fridays, when everything seemed that little bit brighter for one day of the week.

On Fridays, I watch the women from the country doing their shopping, their baskets over their arms, a smile on their faces as they stop to chat in the street. I look at the businessmen and their jackets and them clutching papers to their chest. I see the sailors who have just arrived and the travellers who are going off, carrying heavy cases, taking the one o'clock out of port for Liverpool.

My window faces into the houses and shops of Laurence Street. Beside the dirty butcher's, Ferriter's, is Joe's Fish, his window a bed of ice and the sparkling fish all laid out, ready to be cooked. He is always flat out on Fridays, and he is a good sort, throwing in a few kippers maybe if he has them spare.

Beside the fishmonger's is a narrow alleyway, leading down to three taverns where men hang about all day and night, pissing and shouting and drinking and causing an awful ruckus. You'd see the policeman often there waving his baton, telling them to be quiet, but they never pay much heed, not when they've the drink on them.

Laurence Street is a great location and it isn't. It's the centre of the town, hardly any distance to walk if you want to fetch some groceries or a newspaper or a shawl or a nail. You have the steamer on the quays, five minutes away, which would take you to Liverpool and beyond twice daily – and you have a lovely walk, down along the river, under the Viaduct bridge, where the air would take the cobwebs away from your head.

But the taverns and that alleyway make it a noisy old hole. And the sun never shines on that side of the street. Suits Joe's Fish, I suppose. Number 43 is painted pale blue, an unusual colour on a street of beiges and browns. But I like that blue and its windowsills painted white. Though it is a bit grimy now. Still, it is a refreshing sight in the grey old street, tucked in beside the alleyway and the fishmonger's and the butcher's.

I watched her, walking up the street slowly that Friday, her head bobbing a bit as she looked back and forth, searching for a house. She had to retrace her steps when she saw that she was at Number 45, the house next door which was taller and had more elaborate windows. They were always fancy, the Sullivans at Number 45.

Back she went to Number 43. Rat-tat-tat on the door. I noticed the hat, perched on the side of her head, a small dainty affair. Aye, she was prim and proper, her, the way she held herself all straight.

It struck me that there was something familiar about her, as though I'd seen her before. The angle of her face – or maybe her chin, the way she held it, defiant almost.

I watched as Mrs. McHugh opened the door, a look of thunder across her face, making me chuckle. She could be so vexed, Mrs. McHugh, although considering the circumstances I could see why she didn't want to be disturbed.

And in the woman went and that was that. I watched her arrive and I watched her go in.

The new nanny.

At Number 43, Laurence Street.

ﺮﻮﻮ

"I can't put my finger on it, Betty. There's just something not right. Something I feel, here." Mrs. McHugh is pushing the centre of her chest, between her bosoms.

"Arrah, sure there's so much going on, how would you be right?" says I, taking a suck of my pipe. I've smoked a pipe all my life, since my twenties. Others went for the snuff, but I loved the pipe, the smell of it, the shape of it, tapping the tobacco into it and feeling the heat of it as I lit it up. Nothing more comforting than the smell of a pipe and the feel of it between your teeth, resting on your lip.

"There's something about her, something I don't like."

"Maybe you're jealous?" says I.

Mrs. McHugh scowls.

I feel the smoke from the pipe curl round my face and float over my head. The ceiling above is stained yellowy brown, a tobacco cloud all of my own making.

"Jealous? Why would I be jealous? Of *her*?"

"Well, she's arrived in on top of you and taken over. And haven't you been in charge all these years? Hard to take so it is."

"I'm not jealous," says Mrs. McHugh, sniffing. "And she hasn't taken over. It's more than that. I'm concerned. It's a big responsibility looking after that baby, it's all he has left. How do we know where she's come from? Who she is? Sure, she could be anyone."

"You told me she had references?" says I.

"Aye, but no one we know of to speak for her, to vouch for her. All the way from Dublin? How did she even see the advertisement? It's just not sitting right with me, I tell you, in my gut."

Mrs. McHugh drops by every Wednesday, when she takes her half-day from Number 43. It has become a habit now. At first it started as a kindly gesture after I took to the bed, not able to get out of it at all, and she was forever checking that I was all right, to see if I needed anything. My Jimmy and her Mick had been great old pals.

But lately there's been an awful lot of talk about this nanny. Our weekly chat is now mostly filled with stories about the woman, about things she's said or done or a quare look she's given Mrs. McHugh. I'm growing a bit tired of it, truth be told.

"Sure hasn't she taken the burden of the child from your shoulders? It was too hard for you to manage and the age you're at."

"I was managing very well, thank you!" snaps Mrs. McHugh. "And why does everyone go on as if I'm an aul' one?"

"Because you are," I say, holding on to the pipe with my teeth and giving her a big gummy smile.

There must have been at least twenty-five years between me and Mrs. McHugh. I could have been her mother.

"How much older are you than me anyway, Betty?" says Mrs. McHugh, eyeing me up suspiciously.

"That's for me to know and you to find out," says I, chuckling. "Besides, wisdom comes with age, so I must be nearly full up."

"Well, from one wise old woman to another, what would you tell me to do, Betty, with this nanny?"

"I'd tell you to leave well enough alone," says I. "Things will work themselves out, you'll see." I wave my pipe at her. "Everybody gets what's coming to them. One way or another."

⚬⚭⚬

I haven't left this bed in over a year. It's almost become part of me. Sometimes I don't know what's mattress and what's my legs, what's a pillow or my arms, over my head, down by my side, wrapped under me. Sleeping, dozing, awake.

It's just me and this bed and the world beneath my window. The girl tends to me well enough, but she annoys me, presenting me with cooking that would be so much nicer if she just added a bit more salt, or a bit more butter. Things you learn over the years – things she might never learn, by the set of her.

She takes the top blanket and washes it for me. And she washes me too, a bed bath, keeping me clean with a cloth and soapy water and changing my nightdress or my blouse. On good days I wear my blouse. On the days when I just can't be bothered, I stay in that nightdress all day. I wonder what Jimmy would think if he saw me now?

When I was young, I never would have said that I'd end up like this, a crippled old woman in the bed. I was lithe, you see. Long legs. I could run as fast as any boy in my class and catch him too.

William Thomas was a fine looker of a man. I'd known him since he was a boy, he and his brother Marcus brought up in that pale house at Number 43. His brother, though, he went bald early, whereas William kept that fine head of black hair and sideburns.

He's tired-looking now though.

I can't help but think of all the goings-on there over the years. There was old Mrs. Thomas, William's mother. She was forever at the netted window, watching, waiting, for her husband to come home. Sometimes he did and sometimes he didn't.

I miss nothing, you see. I've always watched from up here and, back in the day, when I was in the shop and the pub – well, I knew everything. People spilled their guts with the drink. He was a gambler too. I felt sorry for her, up there at the curtain, twitching, and him out spending everything they had and doing God knows what with whoever he could get a hold of.

Aye, old Mr. Thomas. I didn't have much time for him. But the son, William, well, he was like the mother. Soft, gentle. Not a bad bone in his body. Didn't drink much, never gambled. And he had a lovely wife, Anna Winchester, God rest her. She was lovely so she was. Real bright blonde hair, the type you usually see only in children.

I always liked to see that, a couple as good-looking as each other.

It was very sad what happened to her. Babies brought such sadness. Sure, didn't I know that myself?

And now the Nanny. I still haven't put my finger on who she reminds me of. It's my eyesight, you see – it's not like it used to be. I used to be like a hawk up here, looking down, watching. I'd love to get a proper look at her, at her face. I'm good with faces.

It's been tough on Mrs. McHugh with everything going on since January, tough on all of them. She treated Anna Winchester like a daughter, she did. And the loss of her and then the baby to look after.

But that's life. Love and loss. And babies.

I hope this little babby will fare all right. Mrs. McHugh treats that family like the family she never had. And maybe that's the problem. Maybe if we all kept ourselves to ourselves, there'd be less heartache in the world, less suffering.

But there'd be less love too. Wouldn't there?

# CHAPTER 5

*The House*

It was a fine house. A solid two-storey, with a white façade, standing back from the road all majestic. He knew as soon as he set eyes on it that he wanted it.

He stood looking at it, taking in the wide roof, moss gathered in between the tiles, white frost dusting those nearest the front slope, a chimney at each end. The guttering was broken in parts, but he could mend that easy enough. The front door needed painting as did the white window-frames – five square windows to the front telling of spaciousness within. It was most pleasing to the eye.

The 'For Sale' sign was roughly painted on a block of wood nailed to the pier. A whitewashed wall and hedge ran adjacent to the road, protecting the house from the few passersby that rambled past on their way into the village of Chapelizod and then on into Dublin city centre, or out the other way, deeper into a thick green countryside.

It was a fella down the pub that told him, when he said he was looking. Said he wanted somewhere a bit fancy, he'd been saving, and now with the inheritance through, well, the time was right to see what was out there.

"Jaysus, I know just the place," the man had said. "A fine house out at the Strawberry Beds. I did some work on it this week, a widow looking to sell. Big white house, loads of rooms, big garden. If I had the money, that'd be the one for me."

He'd always wanted something better, something bigger. Pulling themselves out of the tenements had been his ambition since before they'd even got married.

"It won't always be like this," he'd said to her. "One day, we'll be living in the country in a fine big house."

"Will we now?" she had said and smiled.

She liked that he had ambition, it was to be admired in a man. But in the end, it was her side of the family that would change their lives. That little old aunt in England, God bless her – always had a soft spot for her niece. Who could have guessed the fortune she'd built up over there as a landlady in London? And not a soul to leave it to except his missus.

The inheritance was enough to lift them straight out of the tenements. But they had to find the right house first.

The countryside, they were agreed. Somewhere with fresh air and space and no neighbours clambering up the walls beside you. They didn't want to move too far away either – he had work in the city and the kids needed friends.

Now, as he stood here, blowing crisp white breaths into his hands, he wondered if this would be the one to do it. To take the whole lot of them out of the closed-in shuffling, coughing and spluttering all day and all night.

He took a big breath in and smelt the country air. It was dry in the January frost, a scent of pine wafting from the thick copses of trees growing not far from the house. He thought of the yard at the block where they lived, thick putrid mud to their ankles, the lavvy filled with excrement and stinking water. He thought how he couldn't face another summer, when the stench would rise up to their windows in the heat, how it simmered and cooked and it was all you could do but hold in your stomach when you went, to not breathe in the fumes, to be quick about it and get out of there and hope that you could hold off longer until next time.

It was no place to be rearing kids. Here the country air would clear out their lungs. They could run through the fields, take off into the distance, strengthen their limbs climbing trees and chop wood to make rafts to float on the stream he could hear trickling nearby.

The drive outside the front door was mossy and grown over, stones sunken into the ground now covered with patches of frosty earth and grass. Untended hedges sprawled around the edges of the small front garden. He thought how much brighter the place would look if they sheared back some of those bushes, made the place a bit more presentable.

He'd driven the mule and cart he'd bought, a sense of excitement rising in him with every mile, out through the Phoenix Park and down along the Liffey. He could feel it.

31

This was the one.

He parked the cart beside the wall and made his way to the door, knocking on it hard. He wanted to make sure he was heard. The last thing he wanted, after coming all this way, was to have to turn away and go home, not having got inside, to see what lay beyond the peeling wooden door.

After a few minutes the door opened and a woman peered out. Her eyes took him in, tracing his face to his body, back to his face again.

"I saw the sign," he said, hearing his voice sound almost sheepish.

He was nervous now.

"Yes?" she said.

She had a stony look about her, he thought, white-faced and hard but different to the hardened women he was used to seeing all around him in the tenements. This one was a bit haughty, stand-offish, nothing too warm about her at all.

"The 'For Sale' sign?" he said.

"Oh yes," she said, as if suddenly remembering it was there. "Is it for yourself – are you looking?"

"It is," he answered. "For my family and me."

"Right," she said.

The door stayed where it was, her foot against it, not moving.

"I'm busy now," she said. "But if you give me an hour or two, I can show you round then."

His heart sank a little. He'd been hoping to get in straightaway.

"That's all right," he said. "I'll come back then."

"Fine," she said.

He walked back to the cart, hearing the door close loudly behind him. He decided he'd drive on past the house, to follow the road around, explore what lay beyond.

He couldn't help but breathe deeply as he went, taking in the cool air, the earthiness, the large expanse that spread out on either side of him. After a while, feeling anxious, he stopped at a gate and got off the cart. He left it beside the hedge and climbed over the gate into a large green field. He could hear rushing water and he followed the sound until he came upon a wide stream, gurgling its way over flat stones and small muddy banks. All around him were dense trees. The children wouldn't know themselves with this space and fresh air and these waterways and fields to be explored.

He stood by the water and said a prayer.

*Please God, let us have this house. Let my family and me have this luck, this bit of good fortune.*

After walking along the stream for a while, he went back to his cart and rode on deeper into the countryside, following narrow roads with dips and potholes. A rundown tavern appeared at a crossroads and he pulled the cart up and and left it beside the door. A pint would ease his nerves.

The pub was quiet, with only another man with a newspaper supping. He pulled his scarf off and asked the barman what he knew of the white house, of the widow who lived there.

The barman shook his head. "Not much," he said. "That's the Martin house. They had twins, I think. A bit of a shock when he died, sudden like. James Martin, quiet fella."

The man didn't mention the 'For Sale' sign, in case the barman didn't know about that. He felt, if he shared the information, someone else would swoop in and snatch the house from him.

Now that he'd seen it, laid eyes on the place, he had never wanted anything so badly. It seemed as if they already belonged, under its roof, their feet by the fire.

After sipping his pint as slowly as he could, he mounted his cart and made his way back along the country roads, the same way he'd come. As he approached the house, it rose out of its white wintry mist and his eyes fell on the large lean-to shed, attached to the gable wall. His own shed, imagine, where he could keep tools and his mule and have a woodwork bench.

She was an age opening it but, when she did pull back the door, James Martin's widow had a bit of a smile for him, her cheeks flushed.

"Are you from around here?" she asked as he crossed the threshold into a little hall.

"I'm not," he said, standing on black flagstones. They looked like they'd just been wiped down and washed over. "I'm from the city centre – but the missus and me, we've always dreamed of a house in the country."

"Lovely," she said, and he could feel her eyes on his worn jacket, falling to his trousers and the splashes of paint and plaster on them.

It occurred to him that she might think he couldn't afford this place, that he was wasting her time. He cleared his throat and told her with confidence that he'd recently come into a 'bit of an inheritance'.

She gave him a thin smile and led him through a low doorway which opened into a wide kitchen with a range glowing.

He felt his heart soar. Already he could picture his family sitting round the large oak table, squabbling over bread. The stove had a double oven and was three times the size of what they cooked on in the flat – the missus would go mad when she saw it.

She opened a door off the kitchen. "There's a scullery here," she said.

He looked into a room with several large stone sinks and windows overlooking a large back garden.

"And if you come this way, I'll show you the sitting room."

She led him back through the little hall where he ducked under another low doorway and followed her into a cosy room, with worn rugs on the floor. An open fire had been lit, the sticks freshly crackling, the coal just starting to take light. Smoke held in the air.

"Very comfortable," he said, picturing his family perched on the fabric sofas. In their flat they spent most of their time lounging on the bed or arguing over the two wooden chairs they owned. There was an armchair that was always vacated for him. He imagined pulling it up to the fire flickering in the grate here.

He had to have this house.

Upstairs, the rooms were a good size. In the front bedroom his eyes were drawn to two small wooden cradles near the window, both painted white.

Twins.

"Scarlet fever," she said. "Took both of them within a day."

He looked at the cribs and shook his head.

"I'm very sorry."

The barman hadn't said the twins were lost. This is why she was selling the house. Her husband gone, the twins cruelly taken, the house too big, full of memories.

"Now, would you like to see the garden?"

He followed her down the stairs, running his hand down the banister, feeling the quality of the wood. Everything seemed to be beautifully crafted in the house, the opposite of the cheap repairs in the tenements.

She led him back through the kitchen and scullery and out into the garden, the light making them squint as they emerged.

He walked through the damp grass, breathing in the air, imagining himself and Aidan digging. He thought of the crops of onion and lettuce they'd have come the summer. And the rows and rows of potatoes.

"I'd be in the market for a quick sale, if it suited you," he said.

"It would," she answered.

She was standing with her arms folded, her back to the house, watching him survey the garden.

"Everything's still a mess with my husband's accounts and that. Would you be interested in a cash sale? I'd discount the price of course."

For a recently bereaved widow, she looked like a fine woman, he thought. Strong-willed, as though nothing might phase her.

Whatever way she wanted him to pay was fine by him.

He wanted this house. If she asked him to pay her in pennies, he would. Whatever it took. No questions asked.

# CHAPTER 6

*William D. Thomas*

All of her things lay exactly where she'd left them. A perfume bottle stood with its lid off, its crystal top lying beside it. He had held the lid, worried that the perfume from the bottle would evaporate, that over time he would lose the smell of her to the air of the small dressing room. But he couldn't bring himself to stopper the bottle. It looked as though she had just stepped away for a moment, to the bathroom to fetch something, out to the hall to talk to Mrs. McHugh.

A powder puff lay in a shower of powder and when he looked closely he saw the mark of her fingertips. He hovered his fingers over the imprints, imagining her hand in his.

He found he missed things that he hadn't even noticed when she was alive. The scent of her skin. The aroma when she leaned in close to him at night, when he nuzzled her neck before sleep. If he lifted and sniffed her clothes it was there – a smell, her smell, a mix of her perfumes and her sweat.

Now there was no new source of that smell. Only old items that she had once touched or lain in. Items that would soon lose their smell to the air, to the draughts that Mrs. McHugh allowed into the house through her constant window-opening and penchant for dusting. He had told her not to touch his wife's things, but soon the fresh air, sweeping daily into their house, would take with it all the existing smells of his wife. And the only thing he'd have left would be her perfumes. He had poured some on to a handkerchief and put it under his pillow at night. He woke up every morning clutching it.

He came and sat at her dressing table every day. It was where he felt closest to her, where he could sense her, feel her as though she were still here.

He had put off returning to work for weeks. Going back to work meant coming home to a house where she no longer lived, where she no longer met him on the stairs, or sat in their sitting room with her piece of embroidery or turned over and placed her hand across his stomach, wrapping herself into him at night.

There would be no more luncheons when she dropped by the office, brightening up the panelled walls, cutting his day in half with her smile. There would be no more errands, buying small things to amuse her, listening to her thoughts about how they should decorate the nursery or what they could do in the summer with the baby.

He longed to ride out to the countryside, to roam,

away from the town, away from the memories, from the office and the house and the atmosphere that hung low, permeating everything with its sadness, drawing the very breath from his body.

He realised that the thing he missed most was her companionship, her friendship. The conversations they had about everything and nothing. It wasn't that his wife had been a constant chatterer, a woman who loved nothing more but to prattle on. Her manner was quiet, sometimes reserved, but ever so lovely. The things she said were considered, as though she had time to think about everything, to develop her thoughts and look at all sides. He valued her opinion enormously.

But now she was gone. And he was trying to get used to the emptiness that she left. The chasm in their bed. Only his own male smell when he entered their room.

ംരൻ

He had always felt as though there would be great sadness in his life. That he was born into sadness, that things would happen that he had no power over, no control. He carried that sadness around with him, a melancholy.

His mother had always said it about him. "What a forlorn little boy!"

He didn't know what *forlorn* meant – he thought it meant bad – as in naughty. But a governess had shown it to him in the dictionary one day.

"It means sad," she said. "Are you sad, William?"

He'd looked at her and thought for a moment. Naughty wasn't the same as sad. Was he sad because he was naughty?

"No," he said, shrugging. But it was a lie. He was a bit sad. Always, he felt a bit sad.

School held no interest for him. It came with sharp slaps and rote learning and once they'd covered the world map and atlas, it was as though there was nothing else the teacher could say to hold his attention. He would have preferred to have been left alone, to curl up in a chair with a book, an adventure story of pirates and gunrunning and smugglers.

There were two things that made him happy and it was always a good day if he got to do one of those. The first was fishing. The best fish could be caught out along the riverbanks, two or three miles from town, where the waters ran wide and deep and were filled with trout and leaping salmon. The day he got a fishing rod for his birthday with bait hooks and a little worm box was the happiest he could ever remember.

The second thing that brought him joy was the port and the large ships that came in. He had a special viewing spot just beyond the quays, where he could scramble up Sycamore Hill and watch them being guided in by the pilot. He wrote down all the names of the ships in a little notebook and if he could see their cargo – wood piled high on deck, coal, large container boxes or rods of iron and steel – he'd make a note of that too.

On the days when he got to fish or to watch the ships, he would return home feeling lighter. On the days when he didn't get to do those things, he would find himself sitting in his room, looking out the window onto the street, watching the moving heads sail by below.

Why couldn't he be happy like everyone else, he thought. Why couldn't he go about whistling and having not a care in the world, like other people seemed to be able to?

His mother took him to doctors, who examined him

and said he was of sound mind but did appear to be suffering from melancholy and recommended vigorous baths and plenty of fresh air. He took concoctions of syrups and solutions, poured from dark-brown bottles. They made him feel woozy and eventually he shook his head and refused to take any more. One doctor suggested having his adenoids removed but his mother dismissed the idea. William often wondered if he should have got them taken out, as if coughing those red bloody lumps into a bowl would have been like spitting out his sadness.

His father had no time for his demeanour. "*Snap out of it, boy!*" he'd often roar, sending him scuttling out of his way. So, he learned to smile. Smiling was what adults looked for in him. If he smiled they seemed satisfied with him.

Smiling was easy, if you just concentrated on your mouth and pulled up the corners and showed your teeth. He looked in the mirror one day and watched himself doing it, concentrating on forcing his grimace into a proper smile. But his eyes gave him away – there was no light, no shine, no real smile, no matter how hard he tried.

He was a forlorn little boy. With no light to his eyes at all.

❧

When news came through that their father had been found dead in his cabin on the way back from Calais, William and Marcus found themselves in charge of a thriving import-export business overnight. While William comforted their mother and sorted out their father's financial matters, Marcus returned to sea, wild

41

with anger that their beloved father had been taken from them.

They were surprised to find that their father had left the house at Laurence Street to William. Marcus remarked that their father understood that William was unlikely to go anywhere, that he'd always remain at home, working, happy to see out his days in the town he'd been born in.

"Oh, shut up," William had replied. "You know it's so that I'll look after Mother. While you gallivant around the world. At least I have the decency to be here for her. Which is more than can be said for you."

"Always the doting son, weren't you, William?" said Marcus, in a low, barely audible voice.

"Say what you like," said William. "But we all know that it'll be me who stays to look after her while you float about, not giving a damn about anyone else, just like Father."

"Floating about is what built this business, you absolute fool!" said Marcus.

"And I don't intend to let it go by the wayside now," said William.

Two weeks later, when Marcus had returned to sea and their mother had managed to come downstairs for breakfast, William went to the offices of a landlord who owned a number of buildings along the quays and put a deposit down on a much larger office than the one they were in, negotiating the hire of mahogany desks, comfortable padded chairs and filing cabinets.

He hired a man to paint a sign above the office *Thomas Brothers Shipping Company Ltd.* and opened the expanded business the next day. He spent the following months writing letters to every customer they'd ever dealt with and a year later, on the anniversary of their father's death, his accountant declared that they had doubled turnover.

"I'm very proud of you, son," his mother told him, as she lay on her bed, her breathing laboured with the fluid that had built up on her lungs and made her sound as though she were drowning.

"Thank you, Mother," he answered.

He wondered whether he should get a telegram to Marcus, to tell him that their mother was ill, gravely ill, and he should cut his business trip short to come home. As he thought about how he would write the telegram, his mother's words and the ease with which she expressed her feelings towards him rang in his ears. He was glad that she told him she was proud. But he wished that just once his father had been able to say the same thing.

❧

His fingers traced along Anna's dressing table, over brushes and powder, rouge and small bottles of cream. In a drawer he found soft underwear, scattered messily, a tangle of lace and silk. He opened another drawer and poked through the containers.

He knew nothing of women's ways, of their maidservants and the magic they could work. His mother was a beautiful woman, but his father didn't like fuss and she seemed to spend most of her time making herself looking presentable rather than glamorous.

They were at the Christmas ball the night he met Anna, one of the rare occasions that his father had taken their mother. She stood by his side, her face pink, their father drunk and loud.

William had gone to his mother, to talk, to try and occupy her, to ease her of her embarrassment. He hoped as the night wore on, as more gins and vodkas and bitters were downed, that their father would blend in a bit more.

*No one notices when everyone is drunk.*

Anna had appeared, smiling, her tiny frame wrapped in a red silk gown.

"Anna Winchester," said his mother, introducing them. "You remember Mr. and Mrs. Winchester, don't you, William?"

Winchester. No. He couldn't remember. Did they make galoshes? Or Wellington boots?

"Of course you do," said his mother. "We used to visit them, in the country, when you were small. They moved away then, to Bath."

A flash of running through a maze. Of getting lost. Of peering into a pond with large white and orange carp. Of a little blonde girl chasing him.

Anna Winchester.

"How do you do?" he said, and he took her hand to kiss it.

"You certainly have grown," she said, smiling.

She remembered him too. But he could barely remember her – just the house – and the gardens. And the freedom as he ran and ran.

"Your hair is sparkling," he said, smiling, and she touched a diamond slide above her ear and laughed.

"Very festive, isn't it?" she said.

He felt nervous talking to her, she was such a beauty. But he liked that he had met her before, that she had seen him as a child. He felt his impression had already been made.

"Would you like to dance?" he asked as the band struck up a waltz.

"Yes," she said and held out her hand.

He led her to the floor where couples were beginning to move around, gripped tight.

He saw his mother's face as they walked away, surprised that he was so forward, that he had the courage to ask this beautiful woman to dance.

"And what has brought you all the way to Drogheda at Christmas, Miss Winchester?" he asked as they counted out their one, two, three steps.

"My father has retired," she said. "Ireland is our home. He sold up his business in Bath and we've come back to Swinford Hall."

Rifles. The family manufactured rifles, now he remembered.

"Do you remember me," he said. "From when we were children?"

"Of course," she said. "You were the cry baby, I remember."

He looked at her, horrified, and saw the laughter in her eyes.

"I prefer the term 'sensitive'," he said jokingly.

She smelled of musk, a deep expensive perfume.

"You were quiet," she said. "Gentle. Not like that brother of yours – he was always trying to kick me or play tricks on me. Is he here?"

"Yes," he said. "He hasn't changed much. He's dancing – over there."

She looked to where Marcus was waltzing with an attractive brunette.

"I hope he's not trying to kick *her*," she joked.

"I wouldn't put it past him," he said, his face serene. Then he laughed too.

He could feel tiny beads of sweat forming between his fingers.

"I would love to visit Swinford again," he said.

"Of course you should. Bring your mother – she and my mother can reminisce."

"I should very much like that," he said, thinking of how they might escape alone, if their mothers were occupied gossiping.

She looked at him then, taking in his features and he felt a shiver the length of his spine.

If he could marry this woman there and then, he would.

"You're like a ..." his voice trailed off.

"What?" she asked, stopping dancing.

He wanted to say "a Christmas angel", but he couldn't get the words out. He couldn't say it.

"What?" she asked again, her face breaking into a smile now.

The waltz was finished and the band began a festive hymn, "Joy to the World".

He shook his head and walked her back to his mother, his hand cupping her elbow gently.

A Christmas hymn for his Christmas angel.

His fingers touched something metal in the drawer and he drew it out to look at it. It was the diamond slide she'd worn in her hair, the night they met. The diamonds sparkled now again, glittering, catching the light.

# CHAPTER 7

## *The Nanny*

She waited three weeks before making the journey back to the workhouse. There was something about the place that called her.

She left the nursery and walked down the stairs, meeting Mrs. McHugh on her way up.

"Enjoy your half-day," said the housekeeper as they passed.

She said nothing and walked down the rest of the stairs without looking back, though she was aware that the housekeeper had stopped on the stairs and was watching her.

She closed the front door with a bang.

Mrs. McHugh was a blustering old fool. She

reminded her of the workhouse tutor, the one who used to rod them for not knowing the Catechism off by heart. The woman was a self-righteous prig.

She had the same way of talking down to her too. Standing there, hand on hip, her head cocked, all high and mighty. Who did she think she was? For a housekeeper in a small townhouse she had an awfully high opinion of herself.

Still, she was settling in well. She liked her bedroom on the first floor, giving her a vantage point over Laurence Street and West Street, a fine place for taking everything in.

She wondered how long Mr. Thomas planned on grieving. She might ask him to accompany her on an evening walk or even to the theatre soon, saying that she very much wanted to go but did not want to go unchaperoned.

She thought about Mrs. McHugh's face, watching the two of them leave Number 43, together. What a sight that would be!

Still, he was very soft, Mr. Thomas. His grief for his wife was great. She needed to give him more time, get to know him slowly.

She thought about his body, about what lay beneath those fine clothes he wore. She wondered what he liked, where he was ticklish, what part of his skin she should stroke first? All men were flesh and blood. Beneath that rich cloth, that silk and satin, that cologne and coiffure and expense, they all responded the same, when you knew how to touch them, when you found that spot. You just had to go looking.

She walked up the back way, up the steep hill, feeling her legs grow tired on the incline.

There were people making their way to and from small cottages which dotted the sides of the road. Some were merely hovels, thrown together to offer a vague protection from the elements. Wisps of weak smoke poked their way from the holes in the grassy roofs. There were old men and women inside, huddled under rags, others more able-bodied sitting outside with their begging bowls. They were just steps away from the workhouse and their poverty made her throat thicken. The sight of them made her sick.

She turned at the top of the hill and looked back. The factories along the river pumped black smoke from tall chimneys. The smoke caused a dim mist to settle over the town, making it grey and broody. The river wasn't visible from here, but the bridge with its iron criss-crosses poked into the sky.

She took in a breath. She hadn't expected it but being so close now was taking the wind from her lungs. She could feel her heart beating, pounding out a rhythm in her chest.

The back of the workhouse was overgrown. Black elderberry bushes curled out from the top of the wall, hanging down low, moving in the February breeze. Thin spikes of metal poked out from the top of the wall, a warning to anyone thinking of climbing it, and, further down around the back gate, render had been smeared along the ridge and broken glass set into it.

She made her way along the road, close to the wall, fingering the marks she had used to identify where she was going. Her fingers felt the familiar stones, tracing out the path she used to take. There was a flat stone, smooth as a baby's bottom, and behind it a rough granite stone, set back a little in the wall. Beyond that was a jutting-out stone and then two more that formed bumps like handles to grip.

And then she came to it. The two stones that looked part of the wall but, when pushed, would fall back to reveal a small, round hole that a slender body could squash through.

The stones looked as though they hadn't been moved in years. Lichen sat along the edges, solidifying them against the wall. Crouching low, looking around her to make sure no one was watching, she shoved the top stone with her hand. With a bit of effort, the stone dislodged and forged a white hole opening up into the back garden of the workhouse. She sat on the ground and kicked the bottom stone through the hole too.

Taking a last look behind her, she ducked her head and bent low. Wriggling her body, she squeezed herself through, noting how much she had filled out. The last time she'd been through the wall, the edges had barely touched her. Now, they dragged against her back and stomach, her frame filling every inch of the opening.

She pushed herself to her knees and then her feet. The back garden was empty. The grass was overgrown and matted from winter frosts. She looked towards the building, to the windows covered in black bars, counting, seven, eight, nine, ten and there was the window, number eleven, under which their beds had been.

She stood there, thinking of her.

Kitty.

She remembered how they reached on their beds, on tiptoes, looking out, at the sky, at the clouds, searching for birds, for anything to distract themselves at all.

She felt closer to her now. She could almost feel her, hear her small, high-pitched tones ringing, chattering.

Tearing her eyes from the stonework, she looked left

and saw two mounds with short weedy grass jutting from the soil. She walked over to what she had come to see.

And there it was. A small iron cross, pushed into the ground.

Here is where she lay, underneath the earth, with all the others who had been put there. A few short prayers and a pauper's grave.

She knelt and touched the iron cross, the only marker to identify what this patch of earth was.

From her pocket she took the ribbon, yellow, and tied it neatly in a bow around the centre meeting point of the bars.

"This is for you, Kitty," she said out loud. "I'm sorry."

She stood up and touched her face and found there were tears there. She hadn't felt them leave her eyes, hadn't noticed that they had fallen down her cheeks and rolled under her chin.

She wiped at her cheeks with the back of her hand, feeling the wet smudge against the skin, the cold air stinging.

When she was done, when the tears had stopped and she felt something inside shift from her, she turned and walked back to the wall, to her escape, to the hole that had allowed her to come and go from this place as she pleased. As she flattened herself against the earth to wriggle out again, she thought she saw a flash, a swirl, something behind her, a sound of laughter on the wind.

She looked around, but there was nothing, only a solitary blackbird hopping in the grass.

Coming back here had upset her, but it was something she had to do, something that had gnawed at her, underneath, for a long time.

She would write to Christy this evening. She would

tell him that all was well and that things were going according to plan. All she needed now was a bit of time, to progress, to get what she had coming to her in this town of her birth.

It owed her that at least.

# CHAPTER 8

## *Mrs. McHugh*

"Could I ask you, Mr. Thomas – have you thought of a name yet? I was thinking we should be looking to have the baby baptised."

They were standing in the nursery, looking down at the sleeping child. The Nanny had just taken her half-day and Mr. Thomas was finishing up his lunch hour.

Mrs. McHugh was feeling unsettled after the Nanny had been rude on the stairs. She'd a good mind to tell Mr. Thomas that she couldn't cover Miss Murphy's half-day off any more, to make up an excuse to get back at the woman.

Yet she savoured that half-day with the child. It was her one afternoon a week where she could swaddle and hold the baby close, breathing her in, taking care over her bottles and feeds. In those hours she felt reconnected to her mistress, a tension lifting, her nerves at ease. She wouldn't give up that half-day for nothing.

"The truth is, Mrs. McHugh, I wanted her mother to name her. It was something she was so looking forward to."

"Had she given you a name, mentioned anything she liked?" asked the housekeeper.

"She liked Genevieve for a girl. But it hasn't been sitting right with me since ... well, since everything happened. I feel as though we should honour Mrs. Thomas."

"And call her Anna?"

"Yes. But I worry then that every time I look at the child ..." His voice trailed off.

"I think it would be a great honour," said Mrs. McHugh. "A beautiful name, for a beautiful baby."

From nowhere, tears sprang to Mrs. McHugh's eyes. She felt a pang in her chest, a pain that struck her, as an image of her mistress flashed before her eyes. She took in a breath to stifle her sob.

"I'm sorry," she said. "I miss her so. It's such a terrible loss. Such a tragedy."

"Yes," said Mr. Thomas. He offered no comfort, no words, his body stiff, looking down at the sleeping child.

"Anna Genevieve," he said. "That will be her name. And I'll talk to the vicar soon."

"Lovely," said Mrs. McHugh. "That's a lovely name."

The baby made a little sound, as though in agreement with her new name and they both laughed slightly, easing the build-up of grief in the room.

"I must get back," said Mr. Thomas, walking to the nursery door.

He paused, his fingers on the doorknob and turned back to Mrs. McHugh.

"Are you happy with Miss Murphy and her care?"

He'd caught her off guard. She hadn't expected such a question. If she'd been prepared, she might have found a way to express the concerns that had been building ever since the Nanny had arrived.

"I ... well ... I suppose ... yes."

How could she tell him that things just didn't *feel* right? That she was suspicious of the Nanny and the way she had settled the child? That she didn't like how the child continuously slept and a lot of the time seemed listless, even floppy?

Mr. Thomas looked at her carefully before nodding and opening the door.

The moment was gone.

Mrs. McHugh looked at the baby and folded her arms. She couldn't shake the feeling that she had, somehow, let Anna Genevieve down.

❧

That evening, Mr. Thomas spoke to her as she served dessert at the dining-room table.

"You can head off early, Mrs. McHugh. Thank you, for everything."

She smiled. The sincerity in his acknowledgment made the long hours she'd been putting in over the past few weeks worthwhile.

"You're welcome, Mr. Thomas," she said.

She took her hat and cloak from the back hall and buttoned them as she left through the front door. She'd been leaving early most evenings now. Perhaps it was Mr. Thomas's way of making up for all the extra hours she'd put in since January, but it didn't feel like that. Somehow it felt as if she were being ushered out the door.

When she was a part way down the street she turned and looked back at Number 43.

The Nanny was at the window, holding the curtain, staring at her as though in a trance.

They locked eyes before she turned and continued down onto West Street.

What in God's name was the woman looking at?

Maybe she should take the child to a doctor herself, have her checked over, get a medical opinion on her niggly worries that wouldn't go away. Maybe next Friday, when the Nanny was on her half-day and she could do it without Mr. Thomas or anyone else knowing?

She watched a group of children run along the street, kicking a can and yelling at each other. The can slipped from the rocky footpath, onto the smoother road, making a din and clank as it rolled. She looked at the children's bare feet as they scarpered after it, white in the February chill.

Anna Genevieve would never know a shoeless moment. Pampered and coddled, she would have everything a child ever needed, all the love and cherishing in the world.

And Mrs. McHugh would have a significant part to play in that. She would be there to tell the child of her mother, to teach her all about her, to keep her memory alive.

It wasn't really possible that somebody could hurt a child, was it?

"Don't you think she's sleepy? Very sleepy?"

"Babies sleep, Mrs. McHugh."

"But I haven't seen her awake in ... well, it's hours now."

"You're not with her all the hours like I am. She was awake and alert only a short while ago, when you weren't here."

She always had a reason, the Nanny, always a word as to why her care was better than Mrs. McHugh's. But Mrs. McHugh had a feeling, in her chest, a tightness that she trusted, that had never, to this day, let her down.

She was on to the Nanny. And the Nanny knew it.

The doctor would know. He would confirm that there was something amiss.

It was just a pity she'd have to wait until next Friday to see him. She hoped to God nothing happened before that.

⊷⊙⊶

"How were things today, love?"

Mick was seated in his favourite chair in the kitchen, pipe in yellow stained fingers, puffing away on it.

His wife removed her hat, untying the ribbon from under her chin. "Not too bad," she answered, frowning a little. "Things are easing up, I suppose."

"That's good news, love." He leaned back in his chair and sucked on his pipe.

"Yes, I suppose it is," she said.

Their kitchen in the cottage on the North Road was small and warm. The sitting room to the front of the house was now rarely used, the kitchen being cosier and more inviting, but in its previous years, with Mrs. McHugh's parents and their eight children living in the cottage, it had overflowed with bodies sprawling about the armchair and couch, covering the floor, standing at the mantlepiece by the fire.

Every part of the house held a memory.

"What'll you have for tea? The usual?" she asked Mick, after she'd hung up her cloak.

Mick nodded familiarly. Every day, when he used to

work on the docks, she'd made mustard and cheese sandwiches for his lunchbox. With Mick's retirement, he had taken to cooking up spuds and corned beef at lunchtime while Mrs McHugh ate a good midday meal at Number 43. Now, when she came in from work, she made his old favourite lunch for his tea and they sat by the stove, eating their sandwiches, chatting.

She was quiet tonight, thinking.

"Have you noticed me being forgetful?" she asked, looking over her corned-beef sandwich – no mustard for her – she hated the stuff. "You don't think I'm acting a bit strange, do you?"

"No more than normal," he chuckled.

"I feel like I'm forgetting things. Making mistakes."

"I've not noticed anything, love," he said kindly.

"I've lost my best scarf," she said. "I'm so annoyed over it – it's not like me to be careless."

It was a fringed violet-silk scarf that Mick had bought her when they'd travelled to Liverpool a few years ago. She could have sworn it was in her shopping basket only yesterday, but now it was gone.

"I'll get you a new scarf," said Mick.

"You'll have to go all the way back to Liverpool to replace it," she said.

But that wasn't the point. She was annoyed at herself for losing it in the first place.

Maybe she was getting a bit old now for working like this. Maybe, as Mick had been hinting at more and more, it was time she cut back on her working hours, or even, like him, looked to retire.

But what would she do at home in the cottage all day? She'd hadn't worked all those years as an efficient housekeeper to give up now and go home and sit on her backside. There was life in her yet.

"Don't worry, love, a good rest is all you need," said Mick. "Will you be freed up more now, do you think?"

"Oh, probably not," she said, waving her hand at him. "There's still so much to be done, the laundry, the shopping, Mr. Thomas. I'm worried about him. I think he's still in shock, I don't think it's hit him at all."

"Well, of course he's in shock," said Mick. "But you know, love, I'm worried about you too – you're carrying a lot at the moment."

"I know," she said. "But it's my duty. And when I see that little bairn's face ..."

"Yes, it's your duty. But at the end of the day, that's not your baby, Winnie."

She looked at Mick, and felt her eyes flicker, an involuntary squint.

"*I know*," she said, her voice going up. "*I know that.*"

Mick rose from his chair and stubbed out his pipe. He pulled her to her feet, wrapped his arms around her and held her close. She held in the tears that threatened to spill down her cheeks, feeling his strong shoulder against her chin, and his large stomach pressing into her.

# CHAPTER 9

## Betty

I was always a chatterbox. My mother said if there was a short way of saying something I'd take the long way round. I loved words me, loved to exaggerate. I didn't have much education. After the age of twelve I had to stay home when my mother got sick, but I loved scribbling, writing, practising. Even when I was older, sometimes in the shop I'd take out an old copybook and write out bits of books that I read, that I liked. I suppose you could say I educated myself, because no one thought much of educating a girl in them days, not a girl like me anyway.

Do you know how much better you feel after you've shared a joke and a laugh with someone else? As though the world has been lifted off your shoulders, that's how. Well, didn't it suit me grand to marry a man with a shop and a pub, a place where I met people all day long and every night? People said Jimmy knew what he was doing when he married me, that he'd married himself a good businesswoman, someone who would keep the customers talking, so that they'd stay in the shop and pub and spend every farthing they had. Ah sure, what good is money if you can't enjoy it?

We built up the business, Jimmy and me. It wasn't always as good. When we first married and his ma and da were alive, they had the shop like a shed, full of sawdust and straw, everything dirty – sure you could barely see the shelves for the dust. There were sacks everywhere. And mice ran out along the counter in front of customers. Little bastards.

"They have to go," I told Jimmy.

"What have to go?"

"The bloody mice, Jimmy! You can't have them scurrying about under customers' noses!"

"Ah sure, who minds a little old mouse?" he said. He was like his parents, happy to do everything the old way, not seeing why things had to change.

"They're dirty," I said. "They bring disease, and no one wants to see them, especially not when they're buying food."

The next week I saw traps laid down and a week later, after we'd caught twenty-one mice, all grey and different sizes, the little tails twitching on them, it seemed as though Jimmy was paying heed to me.

"Now," I said, "the floor. It needs to be swept. Take out that straw. I don't mind a bit of sawdust, but it's like a bloomin' stable out there, Jimmy, so it is. People want to come in and buy their groceries in comfort. It'll be cleaner. Get rid of the straw, you'll get rid of the mice."

So, the straw was gone and fresh sawdust laid down to catch the rain and the muck that the customers walked in. He was listening to me, was Jimmy. That's when I knew I got a good one. That I would be spending the rest of my life happy with this man.

I still talk to him, you know. Every day. As though he's sitting right here, in his armchair that has the dip of his head like a high moon in the leather. I look around this room where I am now. At the bed we shared with its patchwork quilt. At the fireplace that glows, where we sat when the work was done and things closed up. At the cupboards where the girl prepares the food, where I once prepared our meals, when it used to be just the two of us.

Sometimes I think he is here, that I can feel him, even smell him. Who am I to say he isn't? Who am I to claim that his soul doesn't come back to visit me every day, that maybe it never left?

Jimmy would never scare me. The vision of him couldn't frighten me.

It's more that I frighten myself. Sometimes I don't know what's real or what's in my mind any more.

∽✦∽

I'd say the best thing about this town is the port. Not all would agree, mind. But I see the beauty in it all. The life. The beating heart that brings business and people in and the sailors that swarm the streets.

A lot don't like the sailors. They're afraid of them. Especially the ones with the darkened skin. You'll often catch a person staring. Sometimes I think they're just holding back their hands from reaching out, to touch that skin, to see what it feels like.

I've always had a soft spot for the sailors. They told great stories, you see. They'd been to so many places, places you couldn't pronounce. I'd stand there behind the counter, wiping at a glass, listening as they described islands with sand so white and fine I thought it might be like snow. Seawater so blue you could see right down to the bottom and check if there was anything coming at you, because the waters were full of fish with spines and poison and even sharks, huge big fish with giant teeth that would snap a man in two.

One day I saw a sailor who had shark teeth in a necklace tied about his neck. He handed it round the pub and we all looked at it in awe until some old fella said you'd see the same size teeth on a pike in the River Boyne. That was the jealousy, you see, the fear of the foreigners. Ah sure, what did he know of that lovely-looking sailor who'd captured a real shark and made a necklace from the teeth in its gob.

Jimmy used to joke and say I had a thing for the sailors and that one day he'd come out to the shop and find I'd have run off with one, never to be heard of again, except to get a card from Jamaica at Christmas. That made me laugh. It would only ever be Jimmy for me and he knew that, but it didn't stop me paying heed to the sailors. It was their adventures I was after, not them and their broad shoulders at all.

I was afraid I'd forget those stories, so I started to write them down. At first it was only a few lines scribbled in a copybook. I wasn't very good at writing, you see – really it was numbers you needed in the shop, but I couldn't get those stories out of my head.

After the old copybook was full, I moved on to a lovely notebook, one with a design swirled into it on the front. I don't know where Jimmy got it for me, but he knew that I liked writing and when he gave it to me one Christmas, well, it was the loveliest present I ever got.

I wrote things down as I heard them – not just the stories from the sailors but all the different things people were talking about – the dances and the merriment and fairy tales – and the sad stories too, of babies lost and children hurt and sickness. I wrote about life as I saw it in front of me, as it moved each day, slowly, until you looked back and flicked through the pages and could see a whole decade spin in front of you.

I didn't show anyone my pages – they were for me and no one else's eyes. Jimmy wouldn't touch them, he was real respectful like that. I kept my notebooks in a box under the bed and, when the day was done, I'd take out those pages and I'd fill them up. It was my way of ending the day, of relaxing after the work was done.

Strange, isn't it, the urge to write like that? And when I started I could barely write at all. But that's the power of the mind, you see. I always believed in learning and not letting anyone hold you back or tell you that you couldn't do something. I'd never let someone tell me not to do something. Sure, I'm stubborn as a donkey – Jimmy always said so.

❦

The thing I like about Mrs. McHugh is her straightforwardness. She doesn't carry airs and graces, she doesn't get all caught up with whatnots and nothings. Usually.

I'm remembering now how I met Mrs. McHugh. It was Mick I met first, a great big brute of a man with shoulders so wide and a back so broad he could do the work of two farm horses he could. He drank with all the other dockers who worked along the quays, carrying and offloading, standing out in the weather, rain or sleet or shine.

The dockers always gathered in our pub. You had different groups drinking in different pubs, you see. Some had the carpenters. Others the tailors. The council men liked to gather in the hotel, posh enough for them, with their starched collars and cuffs and red velvet jackets.

We had the dockers and the ship painters and anyone else who did work along the quays. We were a bit up from the quays, mind, but they liked our pub. We'd formed a little community over the years and that's how I got to know some of the sailors, from the trips they did in and out of our port.

My, they earned those drinks those dockers. They'd come in, soaked, having worked from dawn till dusk, lifting and shifting and hanging out by the quays waiting on the ships to come in on the tide. And they worked through the night too, turnings big steamers round so they could be loaded in the morning with cattle or turf or cotton or linen or whatever was being sold off abroad.

I always liked Mick. He had a great big laugh and smile. He wasn't a good-looking man – you wouldn't exactly have run down the street for a second glance at him if you know what I mean – but he was kindly and he was jolly and I'd say they shared a lot of jokes, him and Mrs. McHugh.

I used to chat to Mrs. McHugh when she'd come in to get the groceries. Before she went to work at Number 43, she worked in one of the big houses out in the countryside, but she liked it when she moved to the Thomases as it was close to her own cottage on the North Road. She enjoyed being down the town for the conversations and the socials.

She told me she'd spent years looking after her mother, lifting her in and out of the bed from when she was a young one. And when she died she got her job out in the country house this side of Slane and she travelled out there every day.

She met Mick then and I'd say he encouraged her to get something closer. Hard work in a big house like that and the travelling to and fro too.

I'd say as she got older she probably wasn't able for all that housework she was doing in the Thomases either but she would never say anything or complain – she'd just get on with it, that would be her lot.

I listened to her as she talked about the staff that were leaving and not being replaced at Number 43. She was ahead of her time, was Anna Winchester. She just loved to have the new gadget or the most modern way of doing things and that meant hiring less and less domestics. Anyways, the way I saw it, they were just putting more work on Mrs. McHugh and her getting older and soon it was only her and Ethel left.

❧

With all her straightforwardness and her getting on with things, I am surprised to see her so discombobulated over the Nanny. It isn't like her to get upset – whatever this nanny is doing, it's like she's cast a spell over her.

My eyes wander over my patchwork bed coverlet, with its blues and blood reds, all faded. The blanket has been on the bed for almost sixty years, now washed every so often by the girl, usually after I've spilled some food on it, which happens when you're bedridden and the blanket becomes your table for eating and reading and everything else.

I'm looking at it because Mrs. McHugh is on about the Nanny again, and I'm getting shockin' tired of listening to her crib about her now. It seems there is no other subject for discussion these days.

"Mrs. McHugh, have you said all this to Mr. Thomas? Because, I'll be honest with you now, you're coming in here, week in, week out with more and more stories of what that woman is doing – and I don't know what you expect me to be doing about it, in my bed up here. You need to tell him all this, not me."

Mrs. McHugh, mid-flow in a sentence, stops and looks hurt. She sighs and looks at me in the bed.

"I don't know how to say it. I don't have any ... any proof."

"Why don't you write these things down?" I suggest, thinking of my own stacks of journals, with my musings and my notes and my observations of everything happening all around me. Now that I'm old I sometimes pull the journals out to help me remember things. To check if what I remember is, in actual fact, fact.

"Oh, I don't know," she says, looking all rattled. "Some of it's too silly to write down, it might look stupid. He might think me stupid. If I could just catch her doing something or maybe even in a lie, then I'd have something to go on."

"You could set her up," I say, and I chuckle.

She looks at me aghast and I shrug my shoulders.

"I see her watching," I say. "From upstairs. Every night she's standing at the window looking down. A bit like myself, I suppose," and I chuckle again.

"You'd never catch that one out," she says. "She's a cute hoor."

"Mrs. McHugh! Such language! You're getting old and contrary. Years ago, a young one like that would never have bothered you. I think you should bring your worries to Mr. Thomas. Sure haven't you years of service? Why wouldn't he take what you have to say seriously?"

"I don't know," she says. "There's just something funny going on that I can't put my finger on."

"Well, you have my take on it," I say, keen to change the subject. "Write and tell. Now to nicer things – what are your plans for Easter? Do you have a new bonnet or are you working on your old one?"

Mrs. McHugh looks down at her own hands and I can see the worry in her face. These last few weeks had been hard on her. Maybe I should be more gentle, let her prattle on and get it all out.

Maybe I'll help her out, do a bit of digging on this Miss Murphy, see if I can find out a bit about her. It might help put her mind at ease, bring an end to these conversations going round and round in circles.

And it will give me a little activity, like an investigator or a detective. I was always nosy with a sense for bad news.

And she is bad news, this nanny.

Anyone can see that.

# CHAPTER 10

*The Move*

They moved on a Saturday. The neighbours were sorry to see them go, but all were happy for them. Everyone wanted out of the tenements.

Some of the aul' ones in the basement flats muttered that they'd have no luck moving on a Saturday and could they not go on the Friday? But he couldn't take a day off in the middle of the week and he was lucky to get the day off at all.

Saturday was a grand aul' day for a move. Even the winter sun was shining in the sky that morning, low and half hidden under the cloudy smoke in the centre as he and Aidan journeyed out towards Chapelizod on the mule and cart, laden down with their belongings.

He leaned back, feeling the light on his face. He'd done it. Lifted his family up, got them out of the tenements, given them a life in the countryside. The deal had been done, the money paid.

The excitement among the girls was something else. For days before the move they'd been agitated, giggling and laughing and messing until eventually he had to tell them to settle down or they'd be left in the flat all on their own if they didn't behave themselves.

The cart and mule had to make three trips to transport their life to the countryside. The first time the cart was loaded precariously with the few pieces of furniture they owned – the table, the armchair, their two wooden chairs, and the dismantled double bed. The missus had insisted on a new mattress for the bed. "I'm not taking that stinking yoke with me," she said, when they'd stripped the bed and could see that the mattress was thin and sagging and had questionable stains covering both sides entirely.

The second trip was to bring the children's trundle beds and all the small things: the utensils, the kitchen wares, the few items of clothing they had, their bedding and his tools. The third trip would bring the family – the final journey to start their new life.

When he and Aidan got to the house on their first trip, the widow was there, dressed in black. She stood at the front door, her hands clasped together, a small case at her feet.

They pulled the mule and cart to a halt close to the front door.

"I've left you some furniture," she said as they dismounted.

He went into the house with her to inspect the donated belongings and was surprised to see that the rooms looked the same as when he'd first viewed the house. There were wardrobes and a chest of drawers, beds in the rooms, and in the kitchen she'd left the utensils and cooking pots.

"Don't you need these?" he asked. "For your new house?"

"Oh, I've no need," she said. "And, sure, couldn't your family be doing with it more than a little old widow like me?"

She was far from old – she was younger than him. He would have put her in her late twenties maybe.

"Where will you be moving to?" he asked.

"I'll probably settle with family up north."

He felt sorry for her, young and widowed, the two empty cots upstairs. He wanted to tell her to take the furniture with her, to sell maybe, but then he thought about his own family, how they had five children now with maybe more to come, God willing. It would be lovely to place a new babba into a fine cot like one of those upstairs.

She handed him a set of keys.

"I hope you will be happy here."

"Thank you," he said, thinking how the house had not been so kind to her.

She bid him goodbye and walked off without a backward glance.

"Could I offer you a lift?" he called after her. "We're going that way anyway?"

She turned, looked at the cart and hesitated. Then she walked back.

He helped her climb up to the bench at the front.

He set about loading the cart, Aidan by his side, keen to do his bit.

He locked the front door after they'd managed to get everything inside.

Climbing up beside the woman, he slapped the mule with the reins and they set off.

She was quiet, clutching her brown case to her chest, a small neat hat pinned to her head. He tried to lure her into conversation, to ask about the area, the neighbours, the best place to buy milk, but apart from answering his questions politely she barely spoke at all.

Aidan was uncomfortable, sitting the other side of her, rubbing his hands to keep warm.

"If I were you," she said finally, "I'd keep myself to myself. There's a lot of people poking their noses in round here. They might look like they mean well, and they might come over ever so nice, but my advice would be to keep to yourselves, don't tell anyone your business and don't be letting them in that house for a look around. Nosey parkers are all they are. Keep yourselves to yourselves and you'll be happier for it."

Her words sounded strange to him. In his block, everyone knew everyone's business. All the women chatted, day and night, on the doorsteps, in the hall, by each other's fires. He couldn't imagine not talking to and getting to know the people they were living beside.

The thought struck him for the first time that maybe this change, this upheaval, might be harder than he expected. It could be that they'd be lonely, that they'd miss their friends and the company in the block.

"I'll keep that in mind, thank you," he said.

When they got to the street where the train station was, he reined in the mule and she climbed down, said goodbye and took off walking.

She could have been anyone, he thought, as she blended into the crowd. She could be a nurse or a shop girl or a seamstress or schoolteacher. She could be anyone with her prim ways and her straight back and her little hat perched on her head.

They made their way through the city, weaving through the traffic that was building, to pick up the second load of their belongings. He couldn't wait until the third journey when his wife and children would climb aboard, with smiles and laughter and maybe even a song to help them on their way.

# CHAPTER 11

## Mrs. McHugh

Friday. She was going to bring her concerns to him today. She wouldn't be nervous. She had been a bad choice, the Nanny, a hasty one, that much was evident now.

She would even offer to fill the gap until they found someone new. Someone more suitable. Someone who didn't act like she was lady of the house and she only the help. It must have been the grief. Mr. Thomas was under a cloud, in a daze and couldn't see what was happening right in front of him.

*Going beyond her station*, she wrote on a piece of paper.

She had taken Betty's advice and written down her

grievances. All this moving into a guest bedroom and then setting up home as if she belonged there. Bossing her around, ordering meals and baby things, expecting to be waited on hand and foot. Who did she think she was?

*Being rude*, she jotted down. Giving her the cold shoulder. Not speaking to her, as if she were invisible. It was unsettling.

The third item she wrote down was the thing that bothered her the most. It was also the hardest to explain because on the outside things seemed to be fine. But Mrs. McHugh knew that there was something amiss with the child. She was far too quiet since the Nanny arrived. Remarkably quiet.

*Baby poorly*, she wrote. It was all she could think of to say, because it wasn't as though the child had a fever or cried with colic or anything like that. The problem, as she saw it, was that the baby hardly cried at all. It was always sleeping. And she felt the baby was losing weight – she'd like to get a scales and have the baby checked.

She had made an appointment with the doctor for this afternoon, when the Nanny was on her half-day and Mr. Thomas was back at the office. She'd talk to him before dinner, just before the Nanny came back. She'd have the diagnosis and the conversation with the doctor then – words from a medical man, proof for her worries and fears.

Part of her was looking forward to the revelation, to finally get everything out that had been bothering her. To be able to tell Betty this Wednesday that she'd finally addressed the situation. It would make a great hour's chat altogether.

But in the way it happened, in the end, it wasn't she who asked to take Mr. Thomas aside, it was he who called her. Her first indication that there was something wrong was when the smirking Nanny came to the kitchen to get her, after Mr. Thomas had his lunch, just before the Nanny was to take her half-day.

"Himself wants to talk to you," she said.

Mrs. McHugh was in the back hall, inspecting a set of shoes Ethel had been given to polish.

"To me?" she said, surprised. Why hadn't he rung the bell to get her attention?

The Nanny stood with her arms folded, one corner of her mouth going up in a smile.

"Is it something that concerns you?" Mrs. McHugh asked the Nanny, wondering why she was hovering, acting as if she knew something was going on.

"Nothing that concerns me." And she turned on her heel and walked off, keeping her arms folded.

Mrs. McHugh made her way to the front sitting room, where Mr. Thomas was perched by the fire on the low couch.

"Mrs. McHugh," he said.

She noticed that he did not smile as he normally would, that he looked almost sullen.

"I need to speak with you," he said. He gestured her over towards the fire where she stood in front of him, her arms behind her back. At least she would be able to speak to him now in private, she thought, like she had planned.

"It's come to my attention that all may not be well," he said.

So! He was ready to address things.

"You've had a lot on your plate lately. It's understandable that things may have got on top of you. Is there anything you'd like to tell me? Anything you need to get off your chest?"

It was a strange way of asking the question, but she went with it, her mind trying to remember the piece of paper with all her grievances on it.

"Well, there is something I need to get off my chest actually, Mr. Thomas. I have a few concerns. I've been holding off telling you, but I think now is as good a time as any. I'm worried about the Nanny. About Miss Murphy. I don't feel that she's suitable for this household. I'm worried about her care of Anna Genevieve."

"I see," he said. He looked disappointed, as though she had said the wrong thing.

"Things have been different since she arrived," she said. She was trying to think of the list of points she had put in the notebook, but the writing wouldn't come to mind. She was addled. "She's high and mighty," she said. "Always looking for things."

It was coming out wrong. It wasn't how she meant to say it. She could hear her voice, how it sounded – indignant. It sounded like she was jealous of the Nanny and that wasn't the case.

"I don't like her," she said. "I just don't."

Mr. Thomas looked at her and sighed.

"Miss Murphy has spoken to me," he said. "And frankly, Mrs. McHugh, I'm very surprised at you. I would have thought after all this time and all these years of service ... well, it's all a bit of a shock to me and I'm quite flabbergasted."

She looked at him, appalled.

"I know it can be difficult when somebody comes into an established household – it can take a while to adjust, to understand each other's ways. But to be deliberately rude to her, to make her job more difficult than it needs to be, well, I really am surprised at that, Mrs. McHugh."

Her mouth was open slightly, as she took his words in. The Nanny had spoken to him before she had? What had she told him?

"I'm sorry, Mr. Thomas," she finally answered. "I don't understand what you mean."

"It's been brought to my attention that you have been undermining Miss Murphy. That you are questioning everything she does with the child and making circumstances extremely difficult for her. It seems you believe no one can give better care to the baby than you can, Mrs. McHugh."

"That's absurd," she said. "I've only ever been civil to Miss Murphy. I haven't deliberately done anything. Not at all!"

"Well, this is what she has reported to me," he said. "And there's more. Much more. I really am shocked, Mrs. McHugh, after all this time."

"M-more?" She stuttered, trying to think of what to say. She had planned on reporting all her worries to Mr. Thomas direct. Now, the woman she wanted to complain about had complained about her first, tarring her name. She felt a heat rash rise through her chest, up her neck, creeping to her face.

She watched as Mr. Thomas leaned over and rang the bell that would bring Ethel scurrying from the kitchen. She appeared within a minute, looking anxiously from her master to Mrs. McHugh.

"Will you fetch me Mrs. McHugh's basket from where she leaves it?" he said.

Ethel gave a little nod and curtsy and left the room.

"My basket?" said Mrs. McHugh.

"I know you were very fond of her," he said. "But you could have asked. In fact, I might have considered gifting it to you. I never would have expected it from you, Mrs. McHugh, I thought you were more straight than that."

"I don't know what you're talking about," she said.

"I know grief can do funny things. I've been in the mires myself these past weeks. Not noticing things. I'm in a daze half the bloody time. And maybe that's how I didn't notice. How you've been getting away with it."

"Getting away with it?" she asked. "Getting away with what?" Her shock at this conversation was now turning to frustration. And anger.

"Please don't deny it," he said. "It just makes it worse. It makes the whole thing worse."

Ethel appeared with Mrs. McHugh's basket hanging limply from her hand. From her white face it was clear she sensed that something mighty was happening.

"Give it to her," he said, when Ethel tried to hand the basket to him.

He waved her out of the room and she left quietly, closing the door behind her.

Mrs. McHugh stood holding her basket, desperately trying to work out what was going on.

"Take out what's in there," he said.

She lifted out the knitted square she used to cover the basket – and stared at what lay underneath.

*"My scarf!"*

It was her scarf, the one that had gone missing some time ago, the one that Mick had bought her in Liverpool.

She dropped the knitted square to the ground and pulled out the scarf. As she did, something small and heavy fell out of it into the basket.

It was a walnut box, square in shape.

She put the basket down on the floor and lifted the box out, its beautiful sheen catching the firelight in the sitting room. With trembling fingers, she opened it and saw Anna Winchester's watch – a delicate gold and ivory affair, a piece that Mrs. Thomas had only worn to dances and balls on occasion. Mr. Thomas had given it to her during their courtship. "Time stopped when he gave me this watch," Mrs. Thomas used to joke to her.

"I didn't put this there," she said immediately, glancing up to see his face, serene and sad.

"Isn't that your scarf?" he said.

"Yes, but it went missing weeks ago. In fact, I was going to report that to you because I thought that Miss ..." She realised he wouldn't believe her. "Mr. Thomas, do you really think that I would take such a thing? That I put this watch in my basket? And what a stupid place to put it, if I had taken it!" She went to laugh. The whole situation was ridiculous.

"I would have found it very hard to believe it, Mrs. McHugh," he said. "If it wasn't for this."

He stood up, reached into his pocket and took out a folded letter. He held it out and she took it and unfolded it and found there were two letters, the second of which fluttered to the floor. The letter was from Walters' Jewellers in Sackville Street in Dublin. She scanned it quickly, her heart kicking against her chest.

*Dear Sir,*

*It has come to our notice that an item placed for sale with us is registered and insured to your name and address. We are happy to offer this item for sale. However, we do request that you issue a signed letter stating this fact to meet the requirements of the insurer, contained herewith. We enclose the original letter outlining the request, a copy of which we have taken. We retain possession of the item along with*

*all papers and await further instruction.*
   *Yours faithfully*
   *Finlay Walters*

Mrs. McHugh shook her head again. "I don't understand," she said. "What has this to do with me?"

Mr. Thomas bent and lifted the second letter which had fallen at his feet.

"I believe this is yours," he said.

She took the letter and opened it and saw that, indeed, the letter was in her own handwriting. She read it quickly, shocked at the words in front of her. She had absolutely no recollection of writing it.

> *Dear Mr. Walters,*
>    *Please find one diamond engagement ring that I wish to sell. I am seeking the highest price for the item as possible but urge a quick sale. I have included the original certificate of valuation. Please send all correspondence to the above address and not to the address as registered on the certificate,*
>    *Yours faithfully,*
>    *Mrs. Winnifred McHugh*

The address on the letter was the North Road, where Mrs. McHugh lived in her small cottage with Mick.

"You took her ring," said Mr. Thomas. He was staring at her now, and she could see the crease of anger across his forehead. "You tried to sell it and you were going to do the same with her watch."

"*I did not!*" she said. "*I did no such thing!*"

"The letter is in your handwriting, is it not?"

"It looks like it is, but I assure you I did not write this."

She stared at the handwriting in front of her, looking at the loops of the letters, the small r's that looked like n's.

"I am beyond shocked," said Thomas. "I have been sick to my stomach since the letter arrived. And then Miss Murphy came to me with her report just now. She said things had been taken from her room too. She urged me to check your basket. I am wretched over the whole thing. It really is unbelievable, Mrs. McHugh."

"You must believe me," pleaded Mrs. McHugh. "I did not take that watch. I wouldn't. Or the ring. I've been set up. Mr. Thomas!"

He had stopped looking at her, his eyes now fallen to the rose rug on the floor.

"I never thought it would come to this, Mrs. McHugh, not after all this time and everything that's happened over the years. You've always been a trusted member of this household. But something's changed over the past few weeks. The death of Mrs. Thomas has affected you badly – but to stoop to this ..." He sighed. "Well, I've no choice but to ask you to leave the house. Immediately."

"Leave!" She was stunned and bewildered.

"I have to believe that there was no malice in it," he said. "That it's all been a fit of madness. Grief-induced, perhaps."

Tears stung the back of her eyes. The rash had reddened her cheeks now and she felt a swirl in her stomach, as though she was going to vomit.

"Sincerely," she said. "I did not do this."

"The fact that you can't admit to it is even more worrying," he said. "Please, go. Now."

She stood staring at him for a moment before picking up her belongings and leaving the room. She was reeling, her thoughts crashing, anger beginning to surge through her body. Outside, she found Ethel who was standing near the kitchen, tears in her eyes.

"I'm going to miss you," she whispered. "I'm ever so sorry."

Ethel had obviously, like all good maids, been eavesdropping at the door.

Quietly, Mrs. McHugh took her cloak from its hook and put it on. She turned then and went to walk up the stairs. She would say goodbye to the child, to hold her one last time before all this confusion could be resolved and she was returned, rightfully, to her position in this house.

A gentle cough made her look up and there, standing at the very top of the stairs, was the Nanny, her arms still folded and now a full smirk on her face. She looked down at Mrs. McHugh.

"This is your doing," said Mrs. McHugh. "This won't be the last you've heard from me."

"Goodbye, Mrs. McHugh," said the Nanny and, as the housekeeper turned and walked to the front door, she heard her say quietly but loud enough for her to hear, "and good riddance."

# CHAPTER 12

## *The Clue*

In the dark, a rat scuttled, its paws flitting over faeces and the urine trickling and flowing in the gutter. Small soggy mounds had formed in parts, hills of waste building in the tall tunnel. Beside the gutter were the banks, flat surfaces where, when the rain flowed and during spring tides, the water would rise up like a river. The bricks, cemented in place for almost seven hundred years, were black with wet, the render darkened.

The rat stopped and stood on its hind legs, its nose twitching. For two days the noise had been aching, starting in the morning and continuing until mid-afternoon. It was a deep and unending pounding, powered by a steam engine that took off with a flutter into a high-pitched roll of pistons. The tunnel has been shaking with the vibrations and the shuddering waves were getting worse.

Bits of black render had been toppling from their setting, plopping into the filthy water below. The walls shook as the top of the roof was eaten at, the thick arm of the drill biting and dipping deeper into the bricks.

A small piece of stone flew from the ceiling and landed beside the rat's tail. It scampered, frightened, deeper into the tunnel and away from the racket above. More debris flew, bouncing off the walls, showering the gulley like hailstones.

Suddenly, with a crack and a splinter, daylight tore through the tunnel. It burnt into the dark, as the ceiling collapsed and with it fell the legs of a white mare, her grey dappled legs floundering.

Her scream echoed through the tunnel. The rat turned and stood on its hind legs again, noticing the light highlighting what was dark before.

With the horse fell two wheels of a red brougham carriage, carrying its master and mistress on an excursion to Julianstown. Its passengers now lay awkwardly, wailing from within their confines, trapped where the door was jammed against the collapsed brickwork.

The steam-powered drill was stopped, puffing as it slowed.

From the surrounding streets people rushed to the scene, gathering in a crowd to assist the driver who had been flung from his mount and the passengers who were trapped within the carriage. The horse had a large, bloody gash across her chest, her legs still thrashing and kicking in the murky air beneath.

The driver was unconscious. His head had clipped the kerb and already a large purple bruise was pooling across his temple. The horse's screaming punctured the air, the noise level rising as voices shouted behind the hands that were put to the carriage in an attempt to lift it from the cavity it had fallen into.

The carriage shifted away from the brickwork and someone shouted stop. The door of the carriage was sprung open and arms dangled down to help the terrified mistress from the upended vehicle. The woman, balancing on the torso and arms of her husband managed to climb out, crawling over the door and step of the carriage, collapsing into the arms of a kindly woman who grabbed her on the road and led her away. Fearfully, she looked back to where her husband heaved himself up, using the seat and all his might to pull his body out of the carriage. It took three pairs of hands to hold him and fold him out onto the street.

Its passengers dislodged, the carriage fell a little further into the newly opened hole and the horse went deeper, the whites of her eyes showing.

The harness held the horse in place. A mooring rope was sent for. It arrived, hairy and thick, uncoiled from a moored ship that had sailed from Norway to the quay. The rope was tied to one of the upended wheels, its other end fastened to the collar of a farmer's shire horse, who had been pulling a heavy cart to the ironmonger's in Shop Street. With a count of three, the shire horse was walked on and with it the fallen carriage jolted backwards.

Accompanying the pulling horse were the biceps and hands of labourers, shopkeepers, delivery men and passersby. The road builders pushed hardest of all, their digging after all having caused the hole in the first place.

It took only two attempts to dislodge the carriage, the

horse coming with it, a man holding her bridle and stroking her muzzle to the shouts and heaves of all around. Everyone else stood well back from her legs which were flailing and kicking in fright.

The carriage landed back on the road with a wooden thud and the horse's hooves grabbled as she found solid ground again. The man at her bridle warned the roadworker who went to unharness the horse to leave it until the poor beast had calmed down, otherwise they'd have a runaway on their hands.

Blood flowed from the deep wound on the horse's front, but her legs were not broken and she would not end up in the knacker's yard, not today anyway.

The driver was not having as much luck. He had yet to regain consciousness and his lips were now turning blue. It was suggested he be brought to the infirmary due to his pallor and lack of response.

The woman who had been pulled from the carriage was in a deep state of shock. She was finding breathing difficult and was brought discreetly into a grocer's shop and upstairs to the sitting room where a brew of black tea laced with sugar was prepared. Her husband accompanied her and got her settled before returning to the scene of the accident to check on the horse, the carriage and the man.

Some of the roadbuilders were now standing back at the steam-engine drill, scratching their heads and organising a cordon around the collapsed site.

No one had been aware that there were tunnels so near to the surface of the road. No one could have predicted that their simple repair job to mend a large pothole at the corner of Shop Street would lead to such a catastrophe.

Earlier, news of the accident had spread to a

photographer who was down along the quays, setting up a shot from the bridge as part of an annal he had been commissioned to do, entitled *Towns and Cities of Ireland*. He had gathered up his equipment and run, alongside a young boy who had come to tell him breathlessly of the incident. On arriving at the scene, he had stood back and surveyed the street, picking a piece of footpath to set up his tripod and camera. He'd managed to capture the overturned carriage, minutes before it was pulled to rights and rescued.

He sold the picture to the local *Argus* that day and, later in the week, sold a second, slightly different photograph to *The Freeman's Journal*.

The driver never regained consciousness. He was taken to the infirmary, in the back of a flatbed cart, where they diagnosed a bleed to the brain, on account of a fracture to the skull. He died that night in a white bed, surrounded by his wife and older two children.

The headlines read **Man Dies as Street Collapses in Drogheda** and **Two Injured, One Dead as Tunnel Opens Up in Drogheda**.

The man's employers made a donation of £50 to his family and paid for a granite gravestone.

The council met with its engineers and an inspection was ordered to update the ground drawings for all future roadworks. When the men, carrying lanterns, descended the stone steps, leading to the ancient town tunnels at Laurence Street, a rat scampered by their boots, unnoticed in the dark.

⌘

# Letter of Correspondence

*Gardiner Street, Dublin, March 1880*

Dear Susan,

Well, I am a free man. They let me out a littler earlier than expected.

After all this time it's hard to believe that I can now do as I please. I thought it would be very liberating and it is, but truth be told it has also been strange. I feel the world is a different place and I am a bit left behind.

I have found a job and I have my eye on a place. I am happy for the time being. I will write with the new address.

I don't know about coming back home yet. I don't feel I would be welcome. Maybe you can try to find out the lay of the land?

Don't put yourself out and don't cause any arguments, but it would be nice to know that I could visit sometime.

Maybe mention me to Winnie and see what she says.

Your loving brother,
Christy

# CHAPTER 13

*Christy*

The air felt cool on his skin. He noticed every part of him that it touched – his face, flowing over his cheeks, tweaking his nose. He felt a gentle wind brush past his ears.

Ten years he'd waited for this.

Outside the world was turning, as if it had never stopped. Women with children walked by. Other children, some small, some bigger, gathered in groups in the road, shouting, sitting, skipping.

Delivery boys with handcarts went by. A large carriage laden down with passengers passed. He felt the excitement rise as he walked, down the road, away from Mountjoy Gaol, not looking back.

At last, he was out.

He walked past churches and cottages, townhouses and the gates of the large grey infirmary, enjoying each step of his freedom. He'd been told not to dawdle, so he didn't, but he took everything in.

The girls. The boys. The women.

He passed through Dorset Street and walked down Parnell Square. He looked at the houses, with their brasses shining and windows sparkling. Doors were opening and basements taking in deliveries. Maids were out scrubbing steps. In the cool of the March morning, the scent of Jeyes disinfectant hung in the air.

Waiting horses chomped in their nosebags, brushed hair gleaming against their harnesses. Owning a horse and cab would be grand, he thought. He wouldn't mind doing a bit of driving at all.

Sackville Street loomed large in front of him. Its wide avenue opened up into a plaza ahead. He stopped and stood for a moment just to take it in. What a sight for the eyes, for the senses of a man who had seen nothing but grey, dripping closed-in walls for the past decade.

He stopped and bought a penny newspaper. He'd go and have a cup of tea to read it. A free man could do a thing like that.

The café was warm when he entered. Other men sat, their heads bent low over steaming cups, blowing on them.

He kept his head behind the newspaper, looking over the headlines, taking in the news, getting to grips with the world he had been let back into. Accidents, tragedies, political rows, diplomatic controversies – it was all happening on the pages in front of him.

He turned to the advertisements and asked the café woman for a pencil, marking the 'rooms vacant' and 'men wanted' adverts that appealed. There were rooms and jobs going – he just had to pick and hope Lady Luck was on his side.

He'd go and get his hair cut, he thought, styled into something more than the rough hatchet jobs they'd been subjected to in there. Hell, he might even have a wet shave.

He clicked his tongue against the roof of his mouth and smiled.

Good morning, world, good morning. It's fit and well you're lookin'.

⚬⚬⚬

The woman who showed him the room had deep lines on her face and patchy dyed hair. He expected she'd retired from the game. He wondered whether she still did a bit on the side, opening business up for men like him, who got out after ten years. Still, though, he could probably do better than her. And he would, maybe later, if he felt like it.

"Breakfast is between eight and half past nine. No stragglers. We can do a dinner if you want but there's plenty of options around here."

She didn't want to be cooking. Not for the likes of him anyway.

"This is a respectable establishment," she said, as he looked around at the shabby bedspread, worn lamp and plain wooden chair. "No tomfoolery. No women. No drinking. No fighting."

She looked at him straight. "No women," she repeated.

He smiled sweetly. "Understood."

"You have three days' board paid. If you want to

extend it, you need to let me know by Wednesday evening."

The room was acrid, the sweat of men tasting freedom for the first time ingrained in the peeling wallpaper. He wouldn't be staying here longer than three days.

He took out his belongings from his canvas bag, laying them out neatly. He left his folded clothes on the bed.

From the bottom of the bag he took out a sheet of writing paper, put it on the wooden chair and hunkered down to write with the pencil he'd taken from the girl in the café.

> *My dearest Maggie,*
> *And so I am free. I hope to have new lodgings*
> *soon. I am glad to be out, as you can imagine.*
> *Is the deed done? How are plans progressing?*
> *I will write with my new address,*
> *Your loving*
> *Christy*

He would send it this morning and it might even reach her by this evening.

And now, he would go for a walk.

A free man could do a thing like that.

ᘒᘒᘒ

He watched the jarveys and the cab men, lined up at Stephen's Green. It seemed like a grand job altogether, sitting around chatting in between fares, well covered up in those cabs, a blanket if you wanted it around your knees. Of course, he'd have to learn all the street names and the geography a bit better, but he could do that. He could learn.

Best of all he'd see all sorts. Different houses. The southside.

He left Stephen's Green and made his way along Grafton Street, looking at the wares on offer. He fingered the coins in his pocket. He might buy himself a new waistcoat maybe, it would look good and proper on a cab.

For now, he needed a new jacket or something that made him look employable, less like a man who had been in Mountjoy Gaol for the past decade. He turned off Grafton Street in search of a pawn shop.

"Give me that cap," he said, noticing a grey-and-brown-flecked peaked cap hung up on a perch behind the woman at the counter. It matched the brown jacket and braces he'd picked out.

He would change later and go about his new accommodation and job search. He'd look like a new man, in his new clobber.

A good, working class man. Honest as they come.

*⸎*

"It's not usually a job I'd give to a man like yourself."

"I'm new to the city, I'm just looking for a few bob. Try me out and if you're not happy I'll be on my way."

The cabbie looked him up and down. They were standing in front of a block of stables, cobblestones wet with the spring shower that had just come down upon them.

Horses stuck their heads over the stable doors, tossing them, whinnying. Some had old coats on them, torn in parts.

"It's dirty work," said the man. "But my stable boy's gone to Jacob's. Never thought he'd trade horses for biscuits, but there you go."

Christy had responded to the advert in the newspaper: **Stablehand wanted, experience with horses**

**required.** He knew by the address it was in and around where they stabled the horses for the hackney cabs. They were busy work horses, out on the street at all times of day and night. He'd be driving in no time.

He didn't know much about horses but he knew you couldn't be scared of them, that you had to stand your ground. As long as he was confident with them, he'd be grand, and if it's one thing Christy McCoy had, it was confidence in himself.

"Can you start today?"

"Aye, I can, no bother at all."

"Them clothes are too good – you'll need something more suited to stable work."

"That's no bother."

"There's an apron you can wear in the tack room there – it was the boy's though – it might be too small."

"I'll be grand."

"I wouldn't normally take on a man like yourself, sure you're nearly as old as myself, but I don't have time to muck out them stables today and there'll be a whole new shift coming in now in the next hour."

"I'll get to work then."

The man looked bemused as his new worker took off his brown jacket and wrapped the small apron around himself. He took a pitchfork, went into the first stable and started tossing the hay, separating the muck from the clean bedding.

"Good man," said the cabbie. "Good man."

And he was off. Shovelling shit, his first day out of prison.

No one could say he wasn't a hard worker. No one could deny that at all.

❧

He walked back to his accommodation that evening, satisfied with himself. Tomorrow, he'd go looking for new digs. He was sure he'd find something suitable. Something central. Maybe even with a bit of class to it.

He had the goo on him now. He didn't know whether to go for a drink or go down the Monto. He couldn't really afford to do both until Maggie sent him a few pound. A drink would taste good, sliding down his throat, a nice cold glass of stout after all that mucking out today. But he was tired, and he knew he'd sleep well if he got what was coming to him, after all that time inside, away from the softness of a woman.

He washed himself in his room, splashing the water over his head and face, using soap to wash away the smell of the stable. The stink was in his clothes though, nothing he could do about that.

Feeling smarter, he left and walked slowly down Gardiner Street, taking note of the houses and the women gathering, spilling out onto the street. By Purdon Street, they were catcalling him and he kept his hands in his pockets and his head down, waiting till he saw the right one.

He saw the stockings first. Loose at the ankles. Beautiful ankles in pretty shoes, holding down petite little legs.

He looked up and took in the frilly nightdress she was wearing, her skin exposed at the shoulders, her hair bleached and curled all around her face.

She looked nothing like Maggie.

"Looking for a good time?" she asked.

He noticed the way she stood, her legs pressed together, one ankle bent as if curtsying to him.

He wanted her.

"I might be," he said.

"I have a place down here," she said, nodding in the direction of Faithful Place.

Faithful indeed.

She turned and walked and he followed her, catching up, taking in her tiny back and the curve of her neck under all those curls. She led him into the house, where the door was open, and straight up a staircase into a room upstairs. He could hear someone else at it and it got his blood going.

"What would you like?" she said, staring at him. She had long eyelashes that batted against her cheeks when she blinked. She looked like a country girl.

"Take off your clothes," he said. "Slowly."

And so she started to peel off the layers of chiffon, lace and ribbon, the barely there nightdress falling to the floor. Underneath she wore stockings and a silk corset.

He reached for her, grabbed her. She stepped back with the shock of his lunge, then forward again and kissed him back. She smelled of fruit, some sort of citrus scent.

She was young too, not that young, but young enough to be his type.

He undid her corset at the back, letting his hands wander over her small breasts, then pulled her stockings down himself.

He took her bent over the bed, going at her, hard.

There was no need to lie down, to be soft, or gentle or to even savour this moment.

He was paying her after all.

He might have hurt her, she cried out a bit, but that only excited him more.

Whores. Sent by God, to the Monto, for him.

And yet he thought of Maggie when he came.

# CHAPTER 14

*William D. Thomas*

"She is the picture of her mother, wouldn't you say?" Mrs. Winchester said.

She held the child out, as though examining a piece of china or a valuable prize pup. She brought the baby up close and then further away, trying to focus her eyes on the child's features.

"Absolute picture," she said. "See her little nose there and the shape of her mouth. She will be a beauty, I'd say. Her mother was such a beauty."

The child's grandmother was sighing now, turning her mouth downwards, her breath blowing the small wisp of dark hair at the front of the baby's forehead.

"And the Nanny?" she asked, dabbing a tear that had

appeared in the corner of her eye. "Where did you get her from?"

"The newspaper advert," he said quietly.

He was standing at the far end of the nursery, observing his mother-in-law who had arrived unexpectedly at the house, all flounce and black frills, her maid sitting below in his front room, a tall carriage outside the door.

"Oh," she sniffed. "I could have assisted you with that. There was really no need to take out a newspaper advertisement, William. You could have got anyone showing up. And it lets everyone know our business. It's so common really. Why didn't you wait? I could have sourced a very decent woman from any number of families. The Gilliespies have more than one nanny – as have the McMonacles – they would have been happy to lend us a hand while we searched for a permanent replacement."

"I didn't have time to wait," he said. "She is perfectly fine. She came with references. She's from Dublin and has good experience. I really don't need a headache over this."

"Yes, but it's so vital, William, to get the right one. It will stand to you and the child much better. I'd like to speak with her."

"I'd prefer if you didn't," he said.

"I'd just like to speak with her," she said. "Am I not entitled to talk to the woman who has primary care of my granddaughter?"

He was not in the mood for his mother-in-law and her nosiness and her thousand questions over minute details. Her very presence annoyed him, and he couldn't wait to see her up and leave and close the front door with a bang.

After Anna's funeral, he had resisted all requests from friends who wished to visit, wanting only to grieve alone. Now Mrs. Winchester had turned up regardless. She would not be kept away.

"Please bring her in," she insisted.

Sighing, William left the room to find the Nanny standing outside on the landing, looking quite anxious.

"My mother-in-law, Mrs. Winchester, wishes to speak with you," he said. He shrugged his shoulders in apology and went back into the nursery with her.

"Ah, there you are," said Mrs. Winchester. "Do come over and stand in the light, so I can take a look at you."

The Nanny went to the window, where light streamed in through the panel glass. She kept her arms by her sides.

"Pleased to meet you, Mrs. Winchester," she said. "I'm very sorry for your loss."

"Yes," said Mrs. Winchester. "It's been a terrible blow to our family. And to this little one," she said, looking down at the baby in her arms. "Tell me, Miss Murphy. You were working in Dublin before this?"

"Yes," said the Nanny.

"And the family name?"

"Oh, you wouldn't know of them, Mrs. Winchester – they were just a small family, a small townhouse, like this."

It was an insult. The Winchesters had never expected their only daughter to leave their country estate for a 'small townhouse'.

"I see," said Mrs. Winchester. "And what did they do? Their business?"

"The family traded in metals," said the Nanny. "Before that was another family – I was with them for three years. They were the Colchesters. Mr. Colchester was a horse breeder."

"Oh, Colchester," said Mrs. Winchester. "Dublin, you say? I know of a horse breeder from Dublin."

The Nanny swallowed and paused for a minute.

"They've since moved away, Mrs. Winchester – it must be different Colchesters."

"And what are your thoughts on bottle-feeding, Miss Murphy?" said the grandmother. "Don't you think this little one would be better with a wet nurse?"

William cleared his throat and said, "You know Anna's views on that. It's not for the Nanny to decide."

"Yes, but I'd just like her opinion on it, William. To hear of her experience."

"I think bottle-feeding is quite adequate as long as it's carried out correctly," answered the Nanny. "A wet nurse can be sometimes necessary, but you must make sure that the woman is clean and that she has enough milk and isn't feeding half the town. I've seen that before. I bottle-fed one of the babies in my care some years back, and I believe the formula they're selling now is of better quality. That baby thrived and I expect this one will too. As long as it's done right, there is no need to worry."

Mrs. Winchester frowned.

"And where are you from yourself, Miss Murphy?"

"I was born in this town actually," she said.

"Were you?" said William. "I didn't know that."

"Oh yes, but I moved to Dublin as an infant. I don't have any memories."

"And what did your father do?" asked Mrs. Winchester.

"He was a dock worker," she said. "A foreman on the docks. I believe he worked very close to your offices, Mr. Thomas."

"Well, isn't that interesting?" he said with a smile. "A family connection."

"Have you any concerns, Mrs. Winchester?" asked the Nanny, turning the questions back on the woman, who was now sitting in the light that had spread through the panel glass and was streaming across the skirt of her dress. Dust particles floated in the air. "About my qualifications?"

"I trust you have references?"

"Of course, would you like me to fetch them for you?"

"That won't be necessary," intervened William.

Mrs. Winchester gave a little sigh and handed the baby over to the Nanny. She patted the back of the child's head, tears gathering again in her eyes.

"I think it's time for tea," she said, clutching her black lace handkerchief, one of many she had sewn since her daughter's death.

⁂

"She seems fine for the moment," said Mrs. Winchester, holding her teacup and sipping the scalding liquid. "Perfectly adequate. But, William ..." She leaned in closer, dipping her head towards him. "Wouldn't it make sense to bring the baby to Swinford? We could employ a team of nannies. She could be brought for walks every day in the countryside. Think what the fresh air would do for her. Here she's so cooped up. You all are."

"No," said William, feeling his teeth grit in his mouth.

"It would give you a break too," she said. "Give you some time without a crying baby in the house. Let you concentrate on your work for a while."

William shook his head.

"Anna was always so happy at Swinford. She loved being outdoors, always outside, it was such a job to keep her clothes clean. If her nannies scolded her once, they scolded her a thousand times. In the end we just put pantaloons on her and let her run riot. This baby could enjoy the same, the freedom of a large house. I honestly think, William, if –"

"I said no!"

Mrs. Winchester jumped in fright.

"Goddamn it, woman. She's staying here where she belongs, with me."

She stared at him, in the gloom of the room which was cold and never got the sunlight, watching his face, held in anger towards her.

"She's all I have left," he said.

"Very well," she said after a moment, composing herself and sniffing in contempt. "But I will have you think about it, for all your sakes."

They were silent, the clip-clop of the horses passing by outside clear to hear.

"I have some errands to run," she said eventually, standing and brushing down her skirts. "I will write and I hope to see you at Swinford soon."

"Yes," he said bending to kiss her proffered cheek in goodbye.

If his mother-in-law had her way, she'd adopt the child herself, taking her away from him altogether.

Such a difficult woman, nothing like her daughter at all.

# CHAPTER 15

*Betty*

I remember Anna Winchester when she first arrived into that townhouse. I used to see her hair, golden, at the windows, like a fairy-tale princess I used to think. She'd peer down at the street and I'd look at her and marvel at her beauty.

There's beauty and then there's beauty that shines out from the soul. It was her soul that made her beautiful.

I'd met her mother twice and I can tell you the beauty didn't come from there. She was an awful bustling woman, huge, with bosoms that would eat you up. No, I expect the softness, the gentleness came from the father's side. Though I don't know much about him.

They were a lovely match, William and Anna. I

always thought that. They were a pair. They chose love over status. It can't have been easy for her to marry into that townhouse with her coming from a big sprawling estate that took up acres and acres of land through the middle of Meath. You could see it on the face of Mrs. Winchester when she arrived on her rare visits to Number 43, pulling up all fanfare in that gigantic black carriage of hers, a footman waiting, her nose curled. I expected it wouldn't be long before she had her way and had them taken out of that house and installed into a much grander affair. On Fair Street perhaps. Or even a country villa, out at Baltray or, maybe, if she really got her way, back out into the countryside in Meath somewhere.

But it never came to that. She never got that far. Not with Anna and what happened to her.

Mrs. McHugh used to tell me about them when she called in. She had settled on her weekly visit by then, dropping by first thing after lunch on a Wednesday. She'd come in up the stairs, bringing the *Drogheda Conservative* for me and sometimes a periodical.

"Oh, she's in a terrible mood with him today," she told me one day, not long after Anna and William were married. She let me in on all the secrets.

"Who?" I asked, my ears pricking up. I always love a good argument, me.

"Well, it's all her fault of course – Mrs. Winchester. She wants Anna back out to Swinford for a few weeks, to help her recuperate."

It was around the start of their troubles, I think, around the first time Anna lost a baby.

"She's saying no, but part of me thinks she would like to go out there for a rest and be fussed over," said Mrs. McHugh. "But he won't hear of it, says she's not to be running back to Mother and Father whenever anything goes wrong, that they're married now and this is married life."

"That's not like him." I said. I was surprised to hear of his insensitivity.

"Oh, I think it's just Mrs. Winchester annoying him, you know the way. Putting her foot down. I don't blame him really – you'd want to see the fuss she made the last time she visited, all nose in the air and sniffing and saying wasn't the house very damp, wasn't there a smell of damp everywhere? And sure, hadn't I put fresh flowers in every single room for her arrival? There was no smell of damp let me tell you."

"Do you think she'll go to Swinford?" I asked.

"No, but she's letting himself know that she doesn't like to be bossed about by him. Or her mother, I suppose."

"Oh, I feel sorry for her, pulled in every way," I said.

"Well, you'd understand," said Mrs. McHugh. "About how she's feeling."

"Aye," I said and then quickly changed the subject. I didn't want to talk about my own circumstances, comparing them to Anna's, dredging up old memories that were buried good and deep, way down. "So, you might have a few more visits from Mrs. Winchester?"

"Oh, I hope not," she said, her face wrinkling up. "I bloody hope not, I couldn't cope with that. Could you imagine? Mrs. La-di-da landing in on top of you, sniffing out damp and looking for dust. I don't know where she got that lovely daughter from, I really don't."

"I bet Mr. Thomas doesn't know either," I chuckled. "Mother-in-laws, who'd have them?"

"Not me," said Mrs. McHugh. "One of the reasons I married Mick is because his mother, God rest her, was long dead."

We laugh at the joke, both knowing that Mrs. McHugh would have loved Mick's mother, the way she loved her own mother, because she was part of him. Mick's mother and Jimmy's mother were of the same ilk – decent, hardworking, simple women.

Neither of us would ever have been inflicted with the likes of Mrs. Winchester. But these were the problems of the gentry. Something we knew only a little about.

∞

Over the years, I've developed a habit of looking at my hands whenever the subject of losing babies was brought up. Eyes straight down, look at the knuckles first, the way the bones pop up when I flex them. I watch the sinews move as I curl up my hands, digging my nails into my palms, concentrating on the white scar above my thumb, where I'd cut myself to the bone peeling potatoes in the year I was first married.

Sometimes I think that scar is a physical sign of what is on the inside.

I thought, when I was expecting, that I'd feel different, that I'd have a big change come over me. But I'd had no signs at all, no sickness. It was nearly four months before I was sure, when I could feel my stomach wall hard. It was then I confessed to Jimmy what I thought and by God he was so happy.

Swept me up off my feet, he did. He grabbed me, his arm under my behind, and swung me round behind the counter, my feet nearly hitting off the small handles on the spice drawers.

"*Will ya stop!*" I shouted at him.

He was grinning and he gave me a big kiss, even though Mrs. Gilhooly had just walked in looking for her

110

snuff and newspaper, but he didn't care that she was watching at all.

"That's bloody brilliant," he said.

*Brilliant*. A lovely word. I was brilliant, me, his wife, who was going to give him a child, installing a family in that grocer's and pub, up those stairs in the room where I lay now, filling the place with light laughter and keeping it forever young.

But sometimes life isn't brilliant at all.

I finger the scar on my hand, which has faded over the years into nothing more than a mark. Back in the day you could have identified me by that scar – ridged it was and solid. Maybe I've rubbed it too much in the sixty years I've had it, or maybe my skin is too wrinkled and papery now for it to hold onto the damage.

I sigh with the sadness, trying to push back memories I'd rather remained locked away. I read some of the newspaper Mrs. McHugh has brought, but my mind keeps flipping back to Jimmy, back to the pub below, to all the people that I knew.

I decide to take out some of my journals, for a look. I want to remember. I want to feel what it was like, back then.

I pull them out from under the bed, where I keep them in a neat stack, tied with brown curly string. I pull one from the middle and open it, smelling the scent of the crinkled pages within. I've put news clippings and receipts, a ticket to a show we went to at Mayoralty House and a train ticket when we went to Dublin for our Christmas shopping.

I turn the pages, thinking of that day out in Dublin, when we had cream buns and tea in a little café on Henry Street. The streets were so busy, wide, the vastness of the city so different to our small town – it almost overwhelmed me. Jimmy put his hand on the small of my back, steadying me, as we walked through the throngs, soaking up the cheer in the winter cold.

Towards the back of the journal, some writing catches my eye and I begin to read. I smile when I see I've mentioned that Mick McHugh had a new woman on the go and that 'she seemed grand'. I'll tell her that when I see her next week – Mrs. McHugh.

Below it, I've written about Christmas, about something that happened that year, an incident that shocked us all.

*Some trouble tonight. That lovely seaman from Mauritius was started on by another seaman, from Poland. He was at him all night, till things got loud and Jimmy asked him to leave. That one Mad Maggie had been hanging off the one from Mauritius all evening. I hate to see her in but we let it go, with it being Christmas.*

Mad Maggie was an alcoholic and a scourge. She'd been born with good looks and she used them to her advantage the only way she knew how. For as long as I could remember, she'd been going about, taking up with men who would have her.

It was why she liked the sailors, why she liked our pub, because it was where they drank and they were transient. We'd barred her years ago but sometimes she'd sneak in and we might not see her, or sometimes, like that night, it was Christmas and we just let her away with it.

I read on, my notes bringing back the terrible sight that greeted us after we'd heard shouting, after Jimmy had put Mad Maggie and the quarrelsome sailor out.

*Well, didn't she pull a knife on the sailor outside. We heard a load of screaming and ruckus and when we came out she'd stabbed him in the stomach with it. The Pole was on the ground, bleeding, and Mad Maggie stood over him roaring into his ear, spit flying and everything, going mad she was.*

I was distraught to see such violence on the street outside our pub. Rows happened, arguments and fights when the drinks went in, but it was rare for something so murderous to happen like that, for a man to lie dying on the street, under the Christmas candle glowing in the big front window. And for a woman to be responsible for it. We always knew Maggie was mad, but we never thought she'd have that sort of badness in her.

*The police came quick enough, but it was too late. The man had bled out, even though we'd brought him back in and tried to stem the bleeding with towels. Terrible night and those poor girls too.*

There they stood, white-faced, shivering, across the road in front of Rosemary Lane, a dangerous place for two young girls to be standing. They watched their mother dragged off, the two arms pulled behind her back, carted off to the station, kicking up and screaming, the streets filled with her racket and noise. It was Jimmy who pointed the girls out to me as I was busy pouring sudsy water onto the street, trying to wash the blood away from the pub, out onto the cobbles of the road.

"Betty," said Jimmy and I looked up to where he was pointing, over at the alleyway at the two girls, hovering quietly.

"Isn't that her daughters?" he asked.

I peered over and tried to make them out in the glow of the lamplight. The smaller one had a big yellow ribbon tied in her hair.

"I think so," I said, and an awful pity came over me.

113

You saw them around sometimes, a haunted expression on their faces, both so pretty, but racked with hunger and hollowness. They followed their mother about, sometimes begging for scraps.

"Should we tell someone?" asked Jimmy, scratching his head, a pained expression on his face.

"We probably should," I said, thinking of where they might be staying, where Mad Maggie had lodgings. No daddy around and now their mother locked up.

"I'll go over and talk to them," he said and I watched as he crossed the road, stepping down off the footpath and heading towards them.

A group of men came out of the pub across the road then, loud and singing, roaring a shanty song.

When I looked back to where Jimmy was headed, I saw the girls had gone.

I turn over the page of my journal and there I'd cut out a picture from the newspaper. They'd printed an image of Mad Maggie and said she'd got twenty years hard labour. I look at her eyes, which were dark, framed with thick lashes, her cheekbones high in her head. And as I study the photograph, as I look at the picture of the woman I'd cut out with my scissors all those years ago, I realise something.

It is the eyes, the forehead, a strong brow, distinct.

Mad Maggie is the absolute image of the new nanny at Number 43.

That was the woman the Nanny reminded me of that first day I saw her, knocking on the door across the street. Mad Maggie.

I try to remember the last time I saw those two girls, before they'd disappeared off down the alleyway before Jimmy could talk to them.

I'll need to get another look, to study the Nanny

closely the next time she walks out the door, pushing the perambulator up the street.

But if you asked me to take a bet, if you said 'Put your money down now on who that woman is', I'd say that I was right and that I'd win that money back, no problem at all.

Mad Maggie was the Nanny's mother, I'm sure of it.

I can't wait to tell Mrs. McHugh.

# CHAPTER 16

## *The Nanny*

Putting the stones back into place – you had to hold the top one in place and shove the bottom one in – she noticed how the lichen had been scraped away at its edges now and, if you looked closely, you'd know someone had been at it.

As she walked away from the workhouse, she tried to push memories of Kitty from her mind.

It did no good to think of her. Coming here was supposed to put an end to all that, to close the circle, loop the loop. She had returned the ribbon and now it would be as if she never existed at all. The only way.

Still, Kitty flashed in her mind. She was such an innocent mite. The tears would spring to her eyes if she saw a dead animal on the side of the road, if she found an insect with a broken wing. She'd crumple when she saw suffering. She was soft as butter left out on a summer's day.

She knew the workhouse would be the ruin of Kitty. That she didn't have what it took to survive it. She knew that she would, in the end, walk out of that place on her own, one day, without her.

Every day, when the morning siren went off, it reverberated off her insides, filling her pounding head, shuddering her body awake. She usually gave an involuntary moan before turning over and trying to block out the caterwauling noise. But it was no good. The siren was designed to rouse everyone from their beds. There was no point in trying to block it out or seek another minute's sleep. The night was over and the day had begun.

They'd make their way to the communal bathrooms, standing in line to wash in freezing water, splashing the scummy liquid across their faces and necks, wiping it with the rag that had been used a hundred times before them. And then to breakfast to queue again and sit at the bench and consume the tasteless gruel, barely sustaining the life within them, licking every scrap from the wooden bowls to try and quell some of the hunger pains that bloated their stomachs and gave them ever-pounding headaches.

Washed and fed, it was time to go to work. The laundry room was already hot and steamy by the time they got there, the great big vats bubbling overnight. The large carts full of the workhouse uniforms, sheets and towels would be pushed in and they would set about unloading it and sorting it and getting it ready for washing, drying and mending.

It was at the laundry that she met him. At the back doors, near to the kitchen, where he came three times a week, helping out on the delivery cart that fed supplies into the great industrial building.

She'd noticed him watching her, felt his eyes on her, on her back when she turned round, over her skinny shoulders and tiny bosom as she faced him, helping to wheel in the detergent and boxes of starch.

She kept her eyes down, but drew them up to sneak a peek, to catch his eyes and then look away, appearing coquettish to him, the way she knew a man liked to be looked at. He held a thin cigarette between his lips and he puffed on it, stopping to tap the ash onto the ground.

"You're new?" he said to her, the cigarette flapping on his lips as he spoke and she could smell it now, the warm familiar tobacco smell encircling her. He was a good few years older than her, old enough to be a man.

"Give us a fag," she said.

"You're forward," he said with a laugh.

She scowled at him and he laughed again.

"You have to earn fags around here," he said.

As the days passed and they began to get familiar with each other, as she opened the heavy doors to take the baskets and supplies into the back hall, she began to let him near her, to allow his hand to rest on her back as he spoke, to touch off his fingers when he offered her those cigarettes, bending her face to his knuckles as he struck the match.

Seeing Christy, waiting for him, seeing his boyish smile, letting him brush off her back and bottom and bosoms whenever she could get away with it, became the highest, loveliest parts of her week. On the days when there were others there, other girls from the kitchen, other men who did the deliveries, they kept their distance from each other and these were bad days because it was harder to sneak a smoke and even harder to touch each other.

She thought how he was the first man she had ever loved. That all the others, all the men her mother had been through, all the layabouts and soldiers and sailors, none of them could compare to him. She dreamed about him at night, about his dark hair that curled behind his ears, the smell of him on her face, on her lips. She began to wake when the siren went off and get up immediately, in anticipation that she might see him that day, that they might embrace, that he might touch her and send shivers through her skin.

If they didn't get to meet, her mood would drop and she'd snap at everyone around her. Even Kitty, bless her, who didn't know why her sister was in a bad mood, but that it happened some days and the best way to deal with it was to keep out of her way and stay quiet.

But those days made the good days even better. It made the days where he moved in and stood close and she could feel him and everything that he was, all the sweeter. And when he made his moves and told her what she had to do to make him happy, well, then it got even better. Look what she could do for him. See how she made him feel, how she was able to make his body shudder like that?

It pleased her that she could do these things for him. And she knew that it was only a matter of time before he came through on his promises, that he could get her out of there, that he could get both of them, her and Kitty, out of there, maybe even go to live with him. He didn't live that far away, he told her, in a cottage that would suit them all grand.

A little palace, he said.

She dreamed of the cottage most nights, the three of them living together, baking and cleaning and going to his bed at night, doing all the things he asked, pleasing him and maybe even pleasing herself. Kitty asleep next door, her belly full of food, going to a local school, no more long heavy days in the laundry.

He was her answer to everything, her escape from there, the one person who could change their lives. And so, she had to do everything she could for him. Whatever he asked. Whatever that entailed.

Standing at the back road, having pushed the stones back into place in the wall, she felt her legs moving and leading her to where they'd always gone when she escaped. The opposite direction of the workhouse, walking out into the countryside.

New houses had been built, a smattering of cottages, whitewashed and fresh-looking, and as she walked on, some larger houses, some two-storey, a pebbledash to the front and cornerstones painted on them. It took money to build houses like that.

The sky parted and a weak sun appeared, burning through heavy clouds that had hung suspended. She looked up into the brightness and wondered if God was shining down on her Himself.

Her heart was starting to pound, tightening in her chest, and she slowed down her pace, in case it was her steps that were causing it. But it wasn't. She knew it was where she was going that was making her whole body tighten in anticipation. It was him.

The walk was longer than she remembered. The road narrowed as she ducked under a stone archway that supported an artery for the train line. She watched the black bushes, concentrating on the entwined branches, looking for birds.

She slowed her pace even more when the house came into view. It was a small cottage in the middle of a row built by the council some years ago to house the needy. The whitewash had turned dark and was chipping off at the front, a scattering of flakes on the ground outside. The mud at the door had hardened in the cold air and puddles gathered in small tracks where footsteps had trodden. Smoke hung in the air around the houses, the smell of something sharp burning, rubbish or scraps, the smell of the poor who burned whatever they could.

There was no movement. No neighbours out. Nobody at the windows.

She remembered what it felt like to come here. Back then it had looked fresher, a few plant pots filled with bright red geraniums at the door. Now only one remained, a large crack in its side, the plant withered in the cold.

⌘

She remembered the night she had slipped in under that lintel, her first visit. She'd knocked on the window and found him, surprised, standing behind the door in his stockinged feet.

"What are you doing here?"

"I came to see you," she said, pushing past him, walking straight into the cottage to survey the room. A small fire burned in a raised grate, bars across it dripping grease where he'd placed four sausages to cook. A black pot bubbled, without a lid. Potatoes.

"So, it worked then?" he asked.

"It worked," she said. She put her hand on her hip and took a good look around the room.

"And no one saw you?"

"No one saw me."

Two rough cupboards stood in the corner, a basin sitting on top. There was no table. A solitary settle stood bench by the fire. The room smelled of damp. Of mould.

"So this is your palace?"

"This is my palace," he said and held his hands out.

"Some palace," she muttered.

Still, the sense of freedom sent bubbles through her blood.

"Have you anything to eat?"

She walked over to the uneven hand-built presses in the corner. He'd mounted flat pieces of wood across them to make a surface to work on. The basin was filled with water, ready for washing.

Opening a cupboard to find a single small plate and a sack of potatoes lying knocked over she closed the door with a bang and said: "I'll have some of them sausages so."

A splatter of grease fell onto the coals and sizzled. He walked to the fire and turned the sausages over to blacken the remaining white slivers. He lifted the lid of the pot and stabbed the potatoes with a fork.

She went and sat on the settle bench, looking at the only door in the room. She wondered if it led to another room, his bedroom, or to outside.

She waited in silence as he prepared the meal, fetching the other plate from the cupboard, spooning out the potatoes, taking the salt down from the mantelpiece and liberally shaking it over their food. There was no butter.

"It's not much," he said, handing a plate to her, "but I suppose the company's not bad." He smiled but she was too busy lifting the potatoes with her hands to even notice.

She ate the sausages, one chunk at a time. Then her giddiness gave way to some nausea. She leaned back, placed her head on the wooden reach of the settle bench and closed her eyes.

"Are you all right?" he asked.

He was sitting right close to her, their legs touching.

"Yes," she said. "It's just nice to ... not be in there."

"How long do you have?"

"Not long," she said. "They'll be round in a while – I've to be back for then."

"Have you time for ..." he said, leaning in to kiss her.

She pulled back. "Now, now," she said, teasing.

"Oh, come on," he said, his voice purring. His hand clamped her thigh and rubbed it.

She turned her head, coyly.

"You know I think about you. When I'm here, in this bed, at night," he said.

He tapped the settle bench. This is where he slept. That meant there was no bedroom so. It was a one-room cottage, the other door led to the back outside, not to another room like she hoped. If she came to live here with Kitty, they'd all be together in this room, squished up.

She turned her head slightly towards him and he took it as his opportunity, gripping her face with his other hand, pulling her chin towards him, kissing her.

The familiar feeling of a man's mouth on hers made her arms and legs clench. She forced them to relax, to lean back, letting him kiss her, passionately.

His hands wandered her body, feeling her breasts under the coarse workhouse dress. There was a scent about him, something lingering that made him attractive. She liked the look of him with his dark hair oiled back and the wide smile that he had, but it was the smell of him, the taste of him, that she wanted.

She lifted her arms so that he could pull her dress over her head.

"Can we put out the bed?" she asked.

He nodded and jumped up, opening out the settle bed and revealing a thin striped mattress and battered pillow.

It smelled of sweat and hair oil.

She took the woollen blanket which was rolled behind the pillow and spread it across the mattress, lying back on it. He lay down beside her, embracing her.

She listened to his panting as he kissed her neck, her breasts, her belly. He pulled all the linen off her to leave her naked on the damp bed. Only then did he start to strip, revealing a broad chest and a slightly pouched stomach.

It was the first man she had ever looked forward to making love to.

And as he rose within her and she too rose to meet him, she looked at the ceiling, gripped him and held.

She remembered it now, that feeling, that sense of togetherness, as though she were not alone, but a part of someone else, whole.

Soon, she would feel that again.

Soon, they would be one again.

⁂

She was tempted to rap on the door, to see if anyone came out, but she knew by the dust ingrained on the window and the raggedy curtain that hung, undisturbed, that the cottage was empty.

Next door, the wiped-down windows indicated life inside.

She startled when the neighbour's door swung open and an elderly man came out, a ring of white hair snipped around his forehead.

"Are you all right?" he asked, friendly enough.

"Grand," she said. "I used to know the man next door."

"Him," said the man. "I hope he never comes back."

The jibe hung in the air between them.

"Ten years hard labour and it's that now. He'll be back any day, I reckon. More's the pity."

He obviously didn't remember her from when he'd seen her sneaking in all those years ago. Nipping by in the dark, running from the workhouse.

Although she looked very different back then.

Sure she was only a child really.

# CHAPTER 17

## Mrs. McHugh

The tears streamed down her face as she walked. She didn't see the people as she passed or take in the familiar townhouses and cottages as she made her way back up the North Road. Children played by the kerb, whooping and crying out to each other, some queuing for a rope swing flung over a lamppost.

She reached home without knowing how she got there, her mind a blur, only William Thomas's angry face and his words running in her mind.

Mick was at the table reading a newspaper and his face fell when he saw hers.

"My love, what's wrong?" he said.

He got up from his chair and it shot backwards on the lino.

He had seen her upset the past few weeks, seen her wretched with tiredness from the new baby, seen her white in the face that tragic and awful day when Mrs. Thomas had unexpectedly passed. But here she was crying again, her face crushed, her emotions seeping out of her. For such a level-headed woman, he had never seen such turmoil.

She went to him and embraced him, shaking with sobs and it was all he could do to put his hands on her and make soothing noises and allow her to compose herself before she could spit out the words behind the tears.

"Let go?" he said in disbelief. "He let you go?"

When she finally got out the story over a cup of sugary tea, she had to tell Mick to sit down and hold on to his arm and tell him he would do no such thing as to march down to Number 43 and make a scene.

"It won't do any good," she said. "You'll just end up breaking something or worse, going for him and where would that get us? Leave it, it'll get sorted, somehow."

She did wish there was a way to fix the situation, to get that nanny and shake the truth out of her.

"I'll talk to Betty, she'll know what to do," she said hopefully.

She couldn't wait to go and see the old woman, to talk to her about what happened, to watch her reaction and listen to what she would tell her to do. She would go and see her first thing tomorrow. If she could bring herself to walk back down that road and step so near to Number 43.

She made another cup of tea but couldn't drink it. It soured in her throat.

"Maybe we should go for a walk. Take your mind off things. Do you remember when we used to go courtin'?"

"Aye," she said.

"What I liked about you then, Winnie, is what I like about you now. No nonsense."

"I put up with your nonsense."

"Aye, but you like my nonsense."

He was quiet for a minute, trying to think of something to cheer her up.

"I've a better idea," said Mick. "Why don't we hire a jarvey, head out for the day? Visit our old haunts?"

"Ah, would you go 'way!"

"Why not? When do we ever get to do something like that? Let's make the most of the day. Sure what else would you be doing, only mopin' round here. It's a grand day. I can go down and fetch a cab. You pack a picnic there, good woman."

He stood up and got his coat.

"Mick," she said.

"I'll be back in half an hour."

"Mick!"

He left, leaving her in the kitchen looking after him.

Bloody Mick.

Slowly she started putting items into her basket, finding a flask and a tin for their sandwiches. She took the thin picnic blanket down from upstairs.

All the while, she went over that day's events in her mind. She couldn't see past Mr. Thomas's face. The anger, seething, holding it back. Worse was the disappointment. How could he think she would betray him like that?

And the Nanny. And that smirk of hers.

How was she going to put things right?

When Mick came back, complete with a hansom cab and driver, she had put on her best shawl. Before they turned the key in the front door, she went back to the kitchen and took two bottles of cider, laying them in the basket and covering it with the thin picnic blanket.

"I hope it doesn't rain," she said, eyeing the sky. "Where are we off to?"

"Monasterboice first," said Mick and he tapped the roof to let the driver know to move off.

It was a thrill to be moving at speed. She hadn't taken a lift like this in so long. It was a real treat to be out like this, just Mick and her, the driver perched behind them, tall, silent, as though he weren't there at all.

They took the road out by Killineer, the hills rising up beside them. Buds had appeared on the trees, patching light green along the dormant branches.

The air was cool and she was glad of the wooden door over their legs, which sealed them into the cab.

"Isn't this romantic?" said Mick and he laughed. "An unexpected day out with my Lady Love."

It was romantic, yes, she thought. But she'd rather have been at Number 43, where she was supposed to be.

"I was thinking," said Mick as the cab turned down towards Monasterboice, the road narrowing and the monastery showing in the distance, "that we should take the steamer, head over to Liverpool again. It's been long time since we did that."

"Going over to buy me a scarf?"

"We could get you a new scarf, aye."

"Well, there's no need now, is there, seeing as I got it back."

"That absolute wench! I swear … if I ever get hold of her …"

"Shush now, Mick."

When they were first married, they went to England every year, a holiday they could afford on account of having no children.

It was on those holidays that she loved Mick the most, admiring his shoulders, moving under the shirt, the way he tugged at his neckerchief as they marched up city lanes and country roads. She warmed when she saw him smack his lips and smile after the first gulp of stout as they sat outside one of the many pubs they came across. It was in those moments that she felt luckiest, lucky that she had found a friend to share her days with, lucky that she had waited until she was older to find this warm, companionable man.

"Still though, it'd be grand, wouldn't it? A trip across the Irish sea?" said Mick.

"Arrah, maybe," she said. Her mind was too addled to be thinking about holidays.

"It would do you good, Winnie, give you a break. You deserve it after everything."

She didn't deserve anything. She couldn't see past Mr. Thomas's face.

"The writing, Mick. It was my handwriting. You should have seen it. I'm starting to wonder now, did I do it? Did I write that letter? Did I do something stupid and I just can't remember?"

"Ah, Winnie."

"I'm serious. Mam went the same. Doing mad things. We'd find the iron in the coal shed and things went missing all the time."

"Will ya stop!"

"I'm just saying. I feel like I've been going mad anyway, losing things. And now this. I'm just wondering could I have done it and I don't even remember?"

"Will you listen to yourself?"

Her eyes filled with tears again.

He turned to her and grabbed her hand.

"We'll get this sorted," he said. "I promise. You're

131

not going mad. I am witness to that. Although the way you're talking, I'm beginning to doubt you a bit now."

He smiled at her.

She leaned into him, the carriage slowing as the road narrowed even more. Green hills in different shades spread out before them, bare of animals, still to be let out into the spring. He was her greatest comfort, a husband she'd never thought she'd have.

She hadn't expected to spend her twenties and most of her thirties tethered to the cottage she grew up in, a slave to a woman who lost a little more of her function every day. The others had helped of course, but as the years progressed and as their mother eventually lost who she was, her person, her dignity, it fell to her to be there, to feed, clothe and wash her, to mind her mother like a baby, to cradle her head when the shadows scared her, or when she woke from a dream where everything had been good again, back into a world where her body and mind were as fluid as water.

And so the years passed. Her good years, the years when she could have got married and felt her own belly swell with a baby. But she couldn't leave her mother, she couldn't commit herself to any man that might take her away from that cottage and the wisp of a woman stuck in the bed.

Mick had been a surprise. A gentle giant, appearing just when she thought the rest of her life would be spent, alone, in the cottage, working out her days for others, no one to come home to in the evenings.

"Here we are," said the jarvey as the cab pulled into the parking bay.

They got out and made their way into the graveyard, blessing themselves as they entered.

Looming ahead was a round tower, dark flat stones

built high into the sky. At the top was a glass-panelled viewing platform, glinting in the sun. They stood for a minute to admire it, the tallest structure for miles to see.

They walked through the gravestones, stopping to read some of the names, wondering if they had ancient family buried out here.

At the High Cross they traced their fingers on the stone, feeling the stories cut there by craftsmen a thousand years before.

"Such skill," said Mick, feeling the tiny stone carvings.

"Hard to believe it's so old," said Mrs. McHugh, imagining the monastery and what it must have been like. Now, stones had fallen all around, walls toppled, the old church in ruins.

"Will we climb the tower? Are you able for it?"

"Are you calling me an aul' one?" she said.

They climbed the small ladder and entered the door of the round tower, which was high above the ground. Inside the tower smelt dank, a faint whiff of urine in the air.

They took their time, climbing the ladders from floor to floor, their way lit by thin slits in the stonework. They stopped to catch their breath, to hold on to each other, remarking and laughing at how their age was catching up on them.

Mick clutched at his stomach.

"I don't know whether I've a stitch or I'm just too old for this, but the stomach's not great today," he said.

"Are you all right?" she asked, concerned.

"I'll be grand," he said.

When they got to the top, they looked out across the land, back towards Drogheda, to the sea, where the whole coastline could be traced.

"Well, you would have spotted the Vikings coming anyway," said Mick.

It was here that Mick had asked her to marry him.

"Do you remember?" he said.

"I do."

"Happiest moment of my life."

"What about the wedding day?"

"Ah, that too."

He kissed her gently and she held on to him tight.

"Right," she said. "No more talk of Number 43. For the rest of the day. I'll forget about it. Until tomorrow."

"That's the spirit," he said.

They were slower coming down, Mrs. McHugh terrified as she backed her ample behind down the ladder. Mick went first, in case she lost her footing.

They took their picnic on a wooden table, offering the cabbie some of their sandwiches. He waved them away and showed them his own in a tin.

Mick tucked into his mustard and cheese sandwiches and smiled.

They could do more spontaneous outings like this now, she supposed. It might suit them after all.

But she couldn't eat her own sandwiches, the tinned beef she'd spread on the bread sticking in her throat. She forced a few mouthfuls down and hoped they'd mute the pit of worry that moved across her insides.

When it was time to go, they climbed back into the cab and she opened the bottles of cider.

Mick slapped her on the thigh when he saw what she'd brought.

"Good woman, Winnie!" he said, taking a slug.

&#8766;&#8766;&#8766;

So much worry. A knot, settling in her stomach.

She'd managed to put it aside for the afternoon and

evening, as they took their cabbie to the tourism spots: Mellifont after Monasterboice, to admire the work of more monk men from centuries ago and then on to Oldbridge, where they got out and stood at the foot of the Obelisk, the rush of the water and the small weirs under the iron bridge loud. They held hands on the way home, enjoying the greenery and the rolling hills rushing by.

But when she got home, after she'd unpacked the picnic and put some potatoes on to boil, it had started to creep in.

The anguish.

As she got ready for bed, she couldn't help the tears that fell, tears of anger. How could he have believed that woman over him? After all these years!

She thought about going to Dublin to the jeweller's that had written about the ring, to get some sort of explanation. That might solve it, to say she'd been set up, to see what they said in return.

But she had an awful fear. What if she got arrested? And worse, what if she really was losing her mind and this wasn't a set-up after all? She'd watched her mother lose a part of herself every day, her faculties slipping one by one. Her greatest fear was that she would go the same. Could it be happening to her already and Mick was protecting her from it?

She knew she'd have to hide her grief and shock from him. If he saw what it was doing to her, he wouldn't be able to help himself – he'd go right down to Number 43 and pull Mr. Thomas up by the collar. Preventing him from doing something stupid was an added burden to what she was already feeling.

In bed, before they turned down the lamp, Mick said, "Maybe we should go to a solicitor? I have a few pound put by – it'd pay for it."

"No," she said. "I'm not wasting money on a solicitor. This is personal between me and Mr. Thomas. I just need to get proof that it wasn't me who did that, who sent in that ring. I need to prove, somehow, that she was behind it. That woman. I think if I let things lie, mull it over, find a way, then I can call to him, when I know she's not there, and try and talk to him. I think I can get him to believe me. I still think he's confused, with all the grief."

"Aye," said Mick. "Maybe. I'd still like to go down and knock his head together for him."

"Ah, Mick!"

"It's not right, Winnie."

"I know. But it'll come right, I'm sure of it."

"You're an optimistic woman."

"Aye," she said. "Optimistic or stupid."

He looked at her and smiled, a moment of humour amid their combined upset, before grimacing and rubbing his stomach.

"Sore again?" she said.

"Aye, it's not letting up."

"Get some rest," she said. "That'll help."

With the light gone out, Mick fell into a heavy sleep, his breathing loud in the room.

She turned over and back again, pulling the covers, unable to sleep with the anxious thoughts in her mind. When she finally drifted off, into a light, fretful sleep, she was awoken, soon after by the sound of Mick vomiting, on the landing.

She got up and came out to him, to find him hunched over a bowl.

"Are you all right, love?"

"Sick as a dog," he said, his voice hoarse. "I've awful pains in my stomach."

"Jesus," she said. "Can I get you anything?"

"Ah, I didn't want to waken you," he said. He stopped, as a wave of nausea crept over him. "Go back to bed," he said. "I'll go downstairs. If I need anything, I'll get you."

She padded back to bed and lay down again, wondering if the cider could have caused it. She'd only had a few sups, whereas Mick had polished off the rest of the two bottles. It had been lying in the cupboard for a while – it must have soured his stomach. If he wasn't better in the morning, she'd go to the chemist's and get him something to settle it.

❦

In the morning Mick seemed a bit better, but he'd been up most of the night and he reported that along with the vomiting he'd been running to the lavvy out the back.

"You poor thing," she said. She settled him in bed and told him she'd go out and get something from the chemist's for him. "Could you manage something to eat. Some toast? Or some soup maybe?"

"Aye, maybe, later," he said. "I'll probably sleep for a bit."

"Grand," she said. "I won't be long."

She made her way from the cottage, her shopping basket over her arm. She hoped his stomach was settling and he'd be better by this evening. It was a pity their lovely afternoon had been spoiled by a stomach bug.

As she walked, she thought about what had happened at Number 43 and how she would take the train to Dublin on Monday. She remembered the name of the jeweller's and the street. She could ask directions to where it was. Mick could even come with her.

She headed towards the centre of town, past the hardware stores that were opening up for their Saturday trade and the haberdasheries setting out their lighter shades for the finer weather coming in.

She had a chat with the chemist, the one on the corner of West Street, who she had come to know well during Mrs. Thomas's care. He recommended a bottle of Fowler's Solution to help settle Mick's stomach and told her to come back if there was no improvement.

When she came out of the apothecary, she looked across the road to Betty's door. She could pop in for a few minutes, to let her know what had happened, to talk through her idea of going to Dublin. She'd tell Betty she couldn't stay long, that Mick wasn't well and she had to be getting home to him.

When she got to Betty's door and turned the handle to open it and go up the stairs like she always did, the girl came down and told her that the old woman wasn't well at all, that she had a fever and the doctor had been called.

"Goodness, do you think it's serious?" asked Mrs. McHugh.

"She's very weak," the girl said. "It's not like her."

"My Mick is sick at home in bed too. Is she vomiting?"

"No, but she's sweating and her forehead is very hot."

Mrs. McHugh stood at the doorway, wondering whether she should go up the stairs.

"She's sleeping," said the girl. "I'll tell her you called."

"Tell her I wish her well and that I'm thinking of her."

"I will," said the girl.

Poor Betty, thought Mrs. McHugh as the girl closed the door. She'd never known her to be sick beyond a few coughs and sniffles over the years.

As she turned to walk away, she couldn't help but look over at Number 43. She wondered what was going on in the household, whether Anna Genevieve was sleeping, whether Ethel had the lunch on.

She should have been in there, right now, making a shopping list, overseeing Ethel wash the floors, getting lunch ready herself.

She saw the curtain upstairs twitch and she turned her head away quickly, not wanting to see the woman.

If only she'd gone to Mr. Thomas sooner. If only she'd put her worries to him, all the niggly signs that the nanny was up to something, maybe she wouldn't be where she was now, walking home instead of to work, her job gone, that woman responsible.

Why had she done it? What harm had she ever done to her?

She couldn't get her head around it. It was most peculiar, that woman's thirst for trouble and torment.

# CHAPTER 18

*Betty*

I couldn't remember ever feeling so unwell. I'd been sick in the past, coughs and colds, sniffles and sneezes. I had a strong constitution though and I prided myself on always being well. I put it down to the great big spoon of cod liver oil I swallowed every day right after breakfast.

But I hadn't eaten breakfast in three days. My head was aching, my heartbeat pulsing in my temples and then the fever came. It washed over me in waves, soaking the bedsheets, sweat pouring from my skin. And then I was gone into a fretful sleep where I didn't know where I was or even when it was.

Jimmy was there. Lovely Jimmy. I missed his hands

and the great big swaddling hugs he used to give me. I felt him hold me again, and it felt so good to hear his voice, to feel him. But in the fever he turned from lovely Jimmy into devil Jimmy, his head twisting and turning like a kaleidoscope. I told myself that I was hallucinating, not to believe that he'd turned like that, but things weren't making sense and then Jimmy was gone and I reached out for him, trying to grab at him, to find him again.

I was back downstairs behind the counter like the old days. Weighing out sugar. Wrapping up butter. Talking to a stream of customers who came at me like lightning. I could hear my voice gabbling, roaring, and I realised in my dream that I was shouting out loud.

I felt someone touch me on the forehead, felt a cool wet cloth there and it felt good. But I couldn't lift my hands to touch it, I was motionless, immobile. And then I was back in the shop, behind the bar this time, listening to black sailors sing shanties and roar 'the high sea, the high sea!'

And then there he was. His little body, his red skin, slowly turning white before me. I watched his tiny toes and the colour drain from them, and I followed it up to his tummy and then to his face.

I watched him go again, watched him pass, lying on the bed in front of me.

And as the roar came out of me, as the sob of grief and disbelief and shock that my baby had stopped breathing right before my eyes, echoed round the room, I saw her.

Standing there.

Mad Maggie.

What was she doing, here in my fever dream, reliving the moment I'd lost my boy?

I prayed for the fever to take me, away out of this room, out of this bed, gone from her and her staring eyes and the lifeless body of my newborn son.

ᏚᎤᏩᏗ

The doctor was called. I knew it was him by his big rough hands. The girl was there too, I heard her say she was shockin' worried.

"Should we move her to the infirmary?"

By Jesus no, I thought. Whatever yis do, don't move me there. Move me there and I'm a goner.

I heard the doctor mumbling but then I couldn't hear any more and I didn't know what he said about the infirmary.

I was tired. The most tired I could remember and all I did was lie in that bed day in, day out. The fever wasn't letting up. It would rage and ease again and come back just when they all thought it might be going.

I saw some quare things over those few days. All my memories jumbled up and coming out as if they were real again. I saw people I hadn't seen in years. I saw my mother. I saw friends I played with when I was a gersha.

Jimmy was there, through it all. I could feel him, sense his presence.

"Hold on," I told him. "I'm not ready for you yet."

But I was so tired, so shattered when I woke that I felt that maybe I was ready for him. I knew, when I went, that I would hold my son again. Who wouldn't want to leave this cripple bed for that?

I lay there in the morning light, a glow around the curtains, blinking.

I was still alive.

I felt as though I'd been through a storm, battered,

143

bruised, every inch of my skin sore, but I was alive.

I was weak though. The girl, her face pale, worried, bless her, brought me watery porridge but I couldn't get it to go down.

"Bring me my pipe," I told her, my voice hoarse.

She did as she was told, muttering that it would hardly do me any good, but as soon as it was lit, as soon as I smelt the embers singe and burn, I began to feel better.

I slouched up in the bed, the pipe in my hand, smoke curling round my head again. Jesus, I loved that pipe. A few sucks on that and I really was feeling like myself again.

"Would you like a cup of tea?" she asked.

"Oh, I would," I said. "I'd love a cup of tea."

And after I drank that, I told her to make me another one and this time to take the bottle of whiskey kept in the cupboard beside the sink and pour a good measure of it into the cup.

I winked at her. She threw her eyes up to heaven, but with the tea, the pipe and the shot of the God liquid, I was nearly right as rain again.

"What day is it, girl, is it near Wednesday yet?"

"It is Wednesday," she said.

"Ah, Mrs. McHugh will be along this afternoon," I said.

"I don't know about that," the girl said, and she moved a bit closer to me. Her eyes watched me sucking on the pipe, and I could see, in that half brain of hers that she was thinking about whether she should tell me something or not.

"What's wrong? Spit it out, girl!"

She looked at the smoke circling round my head, then back to my face.

"I have some bad news, Betty. It all happened over the weekend, but you were too sick to let you know. I'm very sorry to have to tell you."

I felt the pit drop out of my stomach, the way it always did when someone warned they were about to deliver bad news. The dread – searching through a thousand possible situations while you waited on them to open their mouths and announce what the truth of the matter was.

"Mick McHugh is dead. He died on Sunday. He was buried this morning."

I held the pipe, suspended, in between my thumb and forefinger.

"You're joking," I said, which was a stupid thing to say because why would the girl ever joke about something like that?

She shook her head. "I'm so sorry, Betty. Poor Mrs. McHugh. She was in a terrible way. They had to hold her up at the funeral and everything."

My poor, poor friend. She loved Mick, the way I loved Jimmy. And I knew how much losing Jimmy hurt.

I shook my head. I had nothing to say, not to the girl. She looked at me for a minute and asked me if she could do anything for me.

"No," I said.

"She's gone from Number 43 too. She got the sack."

"*What?*" I roared. "*What did you say?*"

She leaned in even closer, her voice dropping to a whisper. "Something to do with stealing so the word goes."

Well, I nearly fell back into my stupor. Mrs. McHugh stealing?

I looked out the window, trying to gather my thoughts. All the talk from Mrs. McHugh about the

Nanny. She must have had something to do with it.

And now Mick dead.

I felt terrible for my friend and for the past few days she'd had and for the days that she had ahead of her now. I'd write her a note, get the girl to deliver it for me, tell her to come and see me, to tell her I was sorry I'd been sick and had been no benefit, no comfort to her at all.

I needed to tell her about my discovery too. About the Nanny, about Mad Maggie.

When the girl had gone downstairs, I took out my notepaper and started to write. I always turned to writing when I didn't know what else to do.

I thought about Mick as I wrote. I remembered him coming in off the dock back in the day, the sweat still wet on his back, his muscles bulging under this shirt from all the lifting and dragging. He said it was all he was good for, that he knew nothing else.

But he was an intelligent man, was Mick. I always thought it was a pity that they'd never managed to have the family they wanted. He would have been a lovely da. Just like Jimmy would have been too, I suppose.

I rubbed the little nub on my middle finger, formed from where the pen rested. I always kept the nib clean, but still ink leaked into that nub, making a navy-blue swirl on my skin. I looked out the window, over at Number 43, thinking about my friend and all the hours she'd put in. All the mornings she'd arrived, to organise the breakfast, the lunch, the dinner, the cleaning, the shopping, the welfare of the Thomas family, the confidante of each and every one of them.

I folded the paper into the envelope.

I roared for the girl. If she went now she could get it up to Mrs. McHugh and she might come down in the afternoon.

How I wanted to talk to Mrs. McHugh! I felt as if I'd been at sea for a month, stuck in this sick bed, cut off from the world. All I wanted was to be able to get out of this bed, to go to her, to tell her I was sorry for everything that had happened to her.

As I heard the girl's footsteps on the stairs, I felt an awful wave of nausea come over me. It seemed to come from my toes and swept through me, rendering me quite dizzy. I put the pipe on the locker.

I went to lift the covers, but my hands were so weak that all I could do was slump down in the bed and lay my head back on the pillow.

The girl came in and right over to the bed. The envelope slipped out of my hand, falling to the floor.

"*Betty!*" she said.

I touched my shoulder, which was paining me, a terrible ache running all the way down my arm, rendering me useless.

"*Betty!*" I heard the girl cry again and now she was shaking me, but it was no use.

I couldn't respond. I could hear her, but it was mixing with a light, a bit like the dreams I'd been having all week.

And then I saw him.

Jimmy. He was smiling, and he looked younger, back in our good days, when we were newly married and fresh and every day was a wonder.

He didn't say anything – he just held out his hand for me.

He wanted me to go with him.

I closed my eyes and the girl's words faded right out of my ears.

And so I went. I didn't look back. There was nothing to look back at.

The bed I'd shared with Jimmy. The bed where my baby was born. The bed where my baby died.

I felt sure that he was up ahead, that all I had to do was walk towards him, sail, sure I was floating almost, it was wonderful.

It was absolutely wonderful.

Angels. The whole lot of them.

# CHAPTER 19

*The Nanny*

Within days of Mrs. McHugh's departure, Number 43 Laurence Street started to show signs of her absence. Groceries had not been bought in. Stains were not scrubbed down. Towellings and clean binders for the baby were not stacked in the nursery like they had been.

Ethel tried her best but, with her workload now doubled and no direction, she struggled.

The Nanny suggested to Mr. Thomas that they would need to fill Mrs. McHugh's position and quickly.

"Yes," he said, but his voice was unsure.

"Would you like me to help with finding someone?" she asked.

He was silent, brooding almost.

"Part of me thinks she'll be coming back," he said. "That we'll get to the bottom of it. I'm going to travel to Dublin this week to collect the ring."

"Oh," she said.

She didn't like his inference that Mrs. McHugh would be reinstated. That was not part of the plan. And she hadn't expected him to travel to Dublin either, to question the jeweller, but no matter.

"Well, we do need urgent help, Mr. Thomas. Ethel is really struggling and with a baby in the house there is need for an extra set of hands."

"Fine," he said. "I'll advertise this week."

"If you like, I could take on more of the house responsibilities, the shopping and the orders, the bills if you like. If we hired another house girl then I expect we would manage just fine."

He seemed to like this idea. And he cheered up after dinner when she surprised him.

"I have a present for you," she said.

"For me?" he said, looking puzzled.

She rose from the table and fetched a brown-paper parcel tied with string from a drawer in the dining-room dresser and placed it in front of him. She sat back down and watched him open it, his eyebrows raised in anticipation.

He unwrapped the package to reveal a journal, a hard-covered book with pages of cream paper to be filled in.

"I thought you could use it as a fishing journal," she said. "I know how much you love to fish. Perhaps you could make more time to do it, now that you have some new equipment."

He pushed back the paper further and found a bait box with room for fishing hooks.

"Thank you," he said. "I am touched. It's a very kind gesture."

She was starting to earn his trust.

On a few occasions, they had got into such pleasant conversations over dinner that he asked her into the sitting room after pudding, and they sat opposite each other, finishing their wine, enjoying the fire.

She always allowed him his silence, not talking when she felt that he just wanted to sit. When the time was right to speak, she told anecdotes and laughed, anything to keep the mood pleasant and show him that she was good company.

She found that when he poured wine at dinner he relaxed and she always encouraged it, getting Ethel to put out the carafe at every meal, telling her to go and get it if she forgot.

They didn't dine together every night. Sometimes, he didn't want dinner at all, and he took to his room, not even seeing Anna Genevieve some evenings.

He was missing his wife. And, she knew, the absence of the housekeeper was affecting him too.

"Maybe we could go with you on one of your fishing trips," she said. "Anna Genevieve and I – I think the fresh air would do her good."

"Yes," he smiled. "Yes, you're right. The next fine day we will do it."

She folded her ankles, coquettishly, and touched her face, smelling the perfume on her wrist, the one she'd been dabbing on liberally from the open bottle on Anna Thomas's dressing table.

"First week in May," he said, "the cruises start on the Boyne. Let's go on a day trip, and take our fishing gear."

"That sounds lovely," she said and smiled.

She would write to Christy that evening.

Everything was going to plan.

She had William D. Thomas exactly where she wanted him.

෴

She thought of nothing but Christy. Now that she had an escape route through the back wall, she didn't have to live for fleeting gropes in the corridor at the back of the wringing wet laundry rooms. The access to him made her think about him even more; she had to get her fill of him, as often as she could.

Kitty was starting to miss her at night. She was wakening now, looking for her, crying. Only that she had a bit of sense not to be making a racket, Maggie might have had to stop her outside visits.

"Where do you go, Maggie?" she asked.

"I go to see a man about a dog."

It was what her mother always said when she was going out late at night and not wanting to tell them where she was really going.

"Are we getting a dog?" asked Kitty, her eyes growing wide.

"Yes, when we get out of here and we get our own house, we can get a dog."

Poor Kitty. She knew when the girl woke and saw that she was gone, she'd fear the worst. That her sister had been taken away or had run away or was becoming their mother with the disappearing act.

"I will never leave you," she whispered. "Even if you wake up and I'm not here, know that I'll always come back for you, Kitty."

They slept together that night, curled into the single bed, Kitty's quick breaths growing deeper as she fell asleep cuddled into her arm.

She felt too, though she didn't like to admit it, that Christy was growing a bit restless himself. She knew by his face when he pulled back the door, how it fell slightly, to see her standing there in her workhouse tunic, a smile on her face, but none on his.

He tried to make out that she should take a break from seeing him. Told her she'd been spotted by that meddling neighbour next door and he was in danger of losing his job over her.

She didn't know what he was making a fuss over. If he lost this job he could get another one. Surely seeing each other was more important than that gossiping good for nothin' next door?

"Will I come here when I get out, me and Kitty?" she asked.

"Here is too small," he said. "We'd have to move somewhere bigger."

"Yes, we could get a bigger house." She smiled. A house, for the two of them and a room for Kitty too. That would be the nicest, warmest thing she could imagine.

And of course, they'd have to get married and live as a proper couple.

She would pester him about when it would happen. Before Christmas maybe. She thought she was about fifteen now, but probably when she was sixteen he'd marry her. That was a good age for marrying, everyone knew that.

She'd cut down on the nightly visits and persuade him over the next while to put their plan into place. After all, she'd been seeing him for a long time now.

It was well time to be getting married.

"Ethel, have you noticed droppings in the kitchen?"

"Sorry, ma'am?"

She had asked her to address her as 'ma'am', doing away with the 'Miss Murphy' that Mrs. McHugh had insisted was more appropriate.

"Mouse droppings, although they may be rat droppings."

"I haven't, ma'am. Why? Have you seen them?"

"Yes. I have. And what's more I noticed a rat in the yard yesterday. I saw it scuttling out there along the back wall. Horrid things."

"Oh, I hate rats, ma'am, hate them!" said Ethel.

"Will you go to Duffy's today and pick up some poison. We'll get it laid down. I couldn't bear to think of them in here, running round the food. Especially with the baby."

"Yes, ma'am."

"Can you go this morning so we'll get it laid out quickly?"

"Yes, ma'am."

"And don't say anything to Mr. Thomas – he has enough on his plate without worrying about rats in the kitchen."

She nodded. "Of course, ma'am, I'll go right away."

⤜⟡⤛

The Nanny had learned the address off by heart – it wouldn't be hard to find – she knew where the North Road was. She took the long way there, walking up Peter Street and down by Magdalene Tower instead of cutting across Bolton Square to lead her to the row of cottages.

She wore a shawl over her head and used it to shield

some of her face. There was nothing unusual about a woman in a shawl, walking, carrying a basket. No one noticed her as she passed, on her way up the North Road.

Boys in short pants and bare feet kicked round a small leather ball stuffed with rags. Their shirts were open at the neck, their complexions ruddy from the hours spent on the road, playing. The girls wore their hair in pigtails, their pinafores grubby and, instead of football, they scratched out a crooked hopscotch and jumped about on one leg, like robins.

When she got to the house, she slipped a large black key from her basket and opened the front door quickly. She stepped into the cottage and closed the door behind her, leaning against it, while her eyes adjusted to the dim light.

The hallway smelled of baking and she could see a small sitting-room off to her right. She made her way to the back of the cottage, where the kitchen was, and saw the source of the warm aroma, where Mrs. McHugh had placed a loaf of brown bread, a loaf of soda bread and a set of scones on the table on wire trays that morning.

Baking before work. She must have been up before dawn.

The kitchen was bare, but neat. Two wooden chairs were tucked under a small table. A cupboard with sliding doors held a basin for the sink and beside it another cupboard lay with a small bowl stacked with salad vegetables and an enamel jug of milk.

Moving quickly, she opened the cupboard doors, searching the foodstuffs for the item she needed. Her eyes scanned the jars and tins stacked there. It was easy to spot the Colman's mustard, standing yellow against the background.

*My Mick loves his mustard. Keeps Colman's in business he does. I never touch the stuff. I hate the taste of it.*

She loosened the lid and peered inside.

*Mick and his mustard sandwiches. I made them every day for this lunch and now I make them every day for his tea. Can't get enough of them.*

The jar was half empty. She took a spoon from her basket and scooped out two spoonfuls until there was just enough mustard for her purpose at the bottom of the jar. She wiped the spoon with a rag and put it in her basket.

*Mick goes out for his walk every day at three o'clock, rain or shine. I think he does be sneaking down to the bookies, but sure he wouldn't be telling me that, now would he?*

From her basket she took a small tin, bright green, with the picture of a rat lying on its back displayed proudly on the front. She opened the lid and heaped three large spoonfuls into the mustard and mixed it through. The white powder disappeared into the yellow.

She looked over the kitchen to make sure nothing was out of place, and everything was just as she found it. She put the jar back into the cupboard and rearranged the items as they had been.

In the sitting room, she looked out the small window, moving the net curtain to see out. A woman was walking up the street and the playing children were still out the front, farther down. She waited until the woman had passed and then scanned the street again before quietly opening the front door, stepping out, and locking it behind her.

She continued her walk up the North Road, pulling her shawl tighter around her head. She would turn back on herself at the Crosslanes, making it a good stretch of a walk. A walk she had told Ethel she needed on account of a headache that had come over her.

"You don't mind, Ethel, do you? Watching Anna Genevieve for just half an hour?"

The Nanny smiled at the thought of what was to come.

Tomorrow, she'd talk to Mr. Thomas, just before she was due to take her half-day.

The letter from the jeweller's had already arrived but she had lain in wait, taken it and hidden it until the right moment to 'deliver' it. It had taken a bit of effort to line up everything just the way she wanted, but being in the midst of it now, halfway there, made her heart soar.

Mrs. McHugh could be gone from Number 43 by lunchtime, if things went well.

Mr. McHugh would be gone by the weekend, Sunday at the latest.

She wondered if she could keep it all a delicious secret. She should wait before writing the letter, confirming the good news.

But she couldn't help herself. She might send a telegram. Telegrams always brought such urgent announcements.

And he had been waiting ten years for this.

# CHAPTER 20

## *The Exhumation*

An owl hovered, its wings silent in the cool evening air. It watched the gravel below for the movement of field mice who came into the graveyard to snuffle among the decaying flowers.

Dropping like a stone, the owl swooped and lifted a mouse from the ground. It carried it to a nearby tree, a low oak, planted in memory of a woman who had died of pneumonia at eighty-three years of age, and swallowed it, the tail hanging, still flickering from its beak, before the final gulp.

Satisfied, the owl sat and dozed, closing its yellow eyes. It opened them again and turned its head almost all the way round as the stillness of the graveyard was broken. Two gravediggers, one tall, one stocky and short, talking, opened the side gate, carrying spades on their shoulders.

They walked to the main iron gates, and pulled them back, the stop of the gate dragging in the hardened mud, casting a perfect semicircle. They waited, still chattering, until a large black carriage appeared and slowed, turning sharply into the entrance of the graveyard. The rumble of the vehicle, quietened their words. The horse whinnied and snorted when the driver yanked its reins to a stop.

From the carriage, five sets of boots dismounted, causing the body of the vehicle to lean towards the ground. It steadied itself back to level, as the coroner, two doctors, the inspector and the clerk of the burial board arranged themselves in the quiet of the graveyard.

Another carriage, smaller and with the words *Dublin Metropolitan Police* painted on its side, rolled in behind.

The gravediggers closed the gates of the graveyard and walked to the assembled party.

"You've marked the spot?" asked the inspector.

"We have," said the small stout gravedigger, who was older and had dug holes to bury hundreds and hundreds of souls.

They followed the gravedigger, hand-lamps swinging in the dark, balancing along kerbstones, showing their respect.

"This is the one," said the man, and pointed to an inconspicuous but fresh enough grave.

"Well, let's get to work so," said the inspector.

The gravediggers pushed their shovels into the soil and began to dig. One of the policemen who had come in the Metropolitan carriage went back to fetch the things they would need.

The two doctors pulled a set of wooden benches together, benches that usually supported the bottoms of the grieving who came to sit and think and pray.

The party stood back as the gravediggers took to the earth, throwing it up in showers of fine clay and small stones.

Soon they dislodged the gravestone and the policemen and the gravediggers lifted it from the ground, grunting with the weight, laying it carefully on the white sheet they had spread on the ground.

They stopped for a few minutes' break, the diggers wiping at their foreheads with rags from their pockets, the inspector stamping his feet impatiently.

Exhumations made him queasy.

"Let's keep going," he said, when he could stand the silence no more.

The pile of earth grew higher, the smell of wet soil and mould filling the air. When the shovels hit the coffin, a damp thud to the wood, they carefully dug around it and applied the ropes. With help from the heaving policemen, the coffin was disinterred and placed, flatly on the pushed together benches.

The clerk of the burial board checked the name plate, as did the coroner.

All put their hands to their noses as the lid of the coffin was prised open.

"Let's get this done quickly," said the inspector, from behind a scarf he had brought for the occasion.

The shroud was torn from the body to reveal a grey, stinking pulp.

The doctors opened their glass jars and took out their instruments. The first doctor put a small handsaw to the head and sheared the top of the skull. He lifted what was left of the brain into the jar proffered by the other doctor. The jar was labelled and sealed with muslin.

Next the doctor separated the centre of the body, drawing a line with his scalpel where the oesophagus should have been. They lifted what they could of the pulp and labelled it *Heart, Lungs, Stomach*. From the lower regions of the body, they took more of the matter and labelled it *Intestines*.

"That's all we can take," said the doctor with the scalpel.

The jars were placed in a wooden crate and given to the coroner. He would deliver it that very night into the hands of the analyst at Trinity College who had already been put on notice.

They put the shroud back on top of the remains and resealed the coffin.

The gravediggers lifted it and lowered it carefully back into the grave and began to shovel the earth on top.

"Thank God that's over," said the inspector who by now was fighting the urge to vomit.

The party waited, with swinging hand-lamps held aloft, until the grave had been fully filled and the headstone put back in place.

Shadows fell across the stone as the men readied themselves to depart.

The engraving on the headstone flashed as the lamps swung.

> **IN LOVING MEMORY OF**
> **JAMES MARTIN**
> **NATIVE OF STRAWBERRY BEDS**
> **WHO DEPD THIS LIFE**
> **18 DECEMBER 1879**
> **MAY HE REST IN PEACE**

৩৫৬৯৯

The black carriage rolled out of the graveyard, led by the Dublin Metropolitan policemen, the coroner satisfied that they had enough matter to examine for their inquest, the clerk satisfied that the exhumation had been carried out legally and his paperwork would meet all of the burial board's standards.

As the inspector clutched his stomach, the gravediggers shouldered the wrought-iron gates and heaved them closed, glad that their task was over and they could go home to their beds.

As they walked out the side gate, an owl swooped low, its wings silent, its eyes searching for mice that may have been disturbed by the digging and the men's feet.

৩৫৬৯৯

## An Updating Letter

*Ballyheath, Kells, County Meath, Ireland*
*April 1880*

*Dear Christy,*
*Thank you for your last letter. It's hard to believe you are out. I'd say you don't know yourself.*

*I'm delighted you have found a job. It will stand to you I'm sure.*

*Yes, I'd imagine it is a little bit strange being free after all these years. I hope you will go slow and enjoy it and get used to it. It's a big change.*

*Let me know if I can do anything for you, or if you need anything at all.*

*I'm not sure if you heard about all the goings-on here, but we got some very bad news there, just two weeks gone.*

*I'm sorry to let you know that Mick took ill and died. They reckon it was tetanus, an infection from a cut in his mouth. He suffered something shocking.*

*We are all very upset about it, especially Winnie as you can imagine.*

*I never saw the man sick a day in his life, strong as an ox he was, but it took him just like that. We were up in Drogheda for the funeral, helping out as best we could.*

*It brought back a lot of memories, being back in the North Road.*

*I did mention you to Winnie but she didn't want to talk about it. I was wondering if a letter to her might be a good idea? Of course, now is not a good time for her, but maybe in a few weeks, she might come round herself.*

*The past is the past and you have done your time now.*

*Write and let me know all your news.*

*If you fancy a visit to Kells, let me know, although maybe leave it for a few weeks until things settle down.*

*Your loving sister,*
*Susan*

# CHAPTER 21

*William D. Thomas*

He could feel the sun burning through a crack in the curtains before he opened his eyes. It cut a line across the eiderdown, searing, hot. It was going to be a beautiful day.

He rose and dressed in a light shirt and cravat, noticing how it was the first day in a long time that he felt he had something to look forward to.

Ethel had prepared a picnic for them with sandwiches and a flask of tea. She'd put some jam tartlets and some scones and butter in the basket and told them to keep an eye out and see if they could pick up some cream at a farmer's stall on the way.

The baby was all ready. He was delighted to see she

was alert and smiling under her white bonnet. A parasol was attached to the perambulator.

"Isn't she bonny?" he said as the baby gave him a toothless smile. He tickled her chin. "I really love to see her smile. I feel I only see her when she's sleeping."

"She's staying awake to see the sunshine," said the Nanny.

They left Number 43, William walking a little ahead of the Nanny, with the picnic basket in his hand and fishing rod against his shoulder. They made their way across the bridge and turned onto the Dublin Road to walk to the train station.

They puffed up the hill, their cheeks turning red in the burning sun. When the workhouse appeared to their right, the Nanny turned her head to the left, to look out over the town.

At the station, they queued for their tickets and joined a melee of people wearing bonnets and straw hats and clutching baskets and cloth sacks.

Stalls had been set up outside the station offering bread, scones, milk and jam.

The Nanny pondered over some blackcurrant jam, turning it over in her hand.

"Put it in the basket, Miss Murphy – today we dine like kings," said William light-heartedly.

She smiled and put it under the linen cloth.

"It's been ever so long since I've enjoyed a day out," she said.

He smiled and thought how he felt the same.

They'd started walking in the evenings with the baby. The only thing that took Anna from his mind was by putting distractions and activities, in the way.

He was starting to learn more about Miss Murphy. She seemed to uncurl herself in his presence, telling him stories, about the children she'd minded, quoting funny things she'd heard them say.

The truth was, he uncurled himself too. He found that taking a walk, with the Nanny and the baby, brought a certain sense of calm.

They folded the perambulator and climbed onto the train at the platform, a thick cloud of smoke billowing across their heads, blocking out the blue sky before evaporating into the sunshine.

The Nanny sat across from him and took the baby on her lap. She looked out the window as the train eased itself out of the station, pointing out things to the baby: tree, cow, birdy. How easy her manner was with the child, how lovely it was to see Anna Genevieve cuddled close to her, her eyes curious.

The journey was a short one, cutting through the green countryside, field after field flying by the window. Dark hedges divided up the land they passed. Insects had come alive in the heat and they scattered as the steam train pushed on over the track.

The chug-chug of the track echoing through the open window was a comfort. He thought how they should plan more trips like this. Dublin was just over an hour away, a journey the baby would be well able to handle.

The last time he had gone to Dublin was to fetch back the ring Mrs. McHugh had sent to the jeweller's to sell. It was a sorry journey, not lessened by the tragic circumstances that had befallen Mrs. McHugh afterwards.

He could well have pressed charges, had her prosecuted for theft. Although he would never have done that. He could never do that do a woman like Mrs. McHugh.

How he missed her kindly smile in the morning and her chatter in the evenings when he came in.

The only memory Miss Murphy would have of the

woman was how it all ended. He couldn't discuss with her how Mrs. McHugh's departure had been like another death to him.

They had gone ahead and hired another housemaid as Miss Murphy had suggested, a quiet girl, Polly, a little older than Ethel.

Miss Murphy saw to the baby and also took over many of Mrs. McHugh's tasks: the household accounts, decision-making, laying down what the two housemaids were to do. She had shown a prowess for leadership. She had stepped into the breach.

And so they settled into a new routine.

Anna Genevieve was becoming more alert now. He was fascinated by her development, watching how she toned her body in preparation for sitting. How Anna would have loved to watch her grow!

They stood up ahead of Beauparc, the noise level on the train rising as the day trippers got ready to descend on the scenic spot.

The sun had risen higher in the cobalt sky.

"Are you hungry?" he asked, when they'd taken everything off the train and walked to a flat part of the grass overlooking the river, where other picnickers had set up.

"Starving," she said.

"Let's eat straightaway then," he said.

They unpacked their picnic and watched as the river steamer pulled up at the dock and families spilled out onto the shore.

"They're going to be busy today. Have you been on one before?"

She shook her head.

"Fabulous day for it. There's nothing more beautiful than the River Boyne on a sunny day," he said.

After the picnic they rested, while Anna Genevieve napped in her pram. He sprawled out on the blanket enjoying the freedom, the fresh air, the light breeze that blew in off the river and ruffled his hair and shirt sleeves.

She sat upright, keeping a distance.

"I expect you might have good sea legs, if your father was a boatman."

"A dock worker."

"Didn't he ever go aboard?"

"I never really knew him, Mr. Thomas."

He sat up on his elbows and looked at her.

"No family left then?"

"No," she said. "A true orphan. I think that's why I became a nanny. I love looking after children and I didn't have any brothers or sisters growing up."

"Must be very hard on you," he said.

"Oh, it's all right," she said. "My mother was wonderful. I got all the attention."

"I got none of it, living in my brother's shadow," he said. "I was ever so pleased when he took to the seas, just like my father!"

He noticed how pretty she looked when she laughed. Her eyes seemed to sparkle in the sunlight and she looked as wistful as a girl. He broke his gaze and picked up the flask to pour more tea.

"Ready to test those water-legs after all?" he asked when the cruiser appeared on the horizon.

"Yes!" she said cheerfully.

They took their fishing rod and left the pram on the dock, beside two others. The queue was long, but they were lucky to take the last seats right at the back, the baby nestling into the Nanny's lap. They felt the cruiser rock under their feet and bump side to side as it left the dock, before picking up speed and setting sail down the river.

On the water, a fine breeze met their faces, easing the hot sun. The boat was topped with a wide roof and they settled back in the scooped chairs, pointing out things they saw to each other. A blue kingfisher hovering at the riverbank. The splash of an otter, its tail disappearing into the water. A large rhododendron in bloom.

After they passed a large country manor, the boat veered left, joining with the narrow canal that ran alongside the river. The water changed from the choppy waves of the river to the stillness of the deep canal, the surface a murky mirror, where they could see their reflections clearly. The boat slowed down, its roof tickled by trailing willow branches.

"It's so beautiful here," said the Nanny.

Walkers strolling along the canal path waved as the boat sailed by. Ladies in wide summer dresses held small children's hands, gentleman in light suits accompanying them.

They passed under the small stone bridge at Oldbridge, before reaching the lock, where they had to wait for the water to tumble down and raise them up to the level of the road.

"Let's get out here," he said.

They wobbled up to the gate and the boatman put his leg on the pier so that they could get off. The Nanny held the baby tight to her chest and reached for William's hand to step onto the bank.

It was the first time they had ever touched.

They walked back the way the boat had come, searching for a good fishing point.

"There used to be a great spot," he said, looking ahead. "I think it's up there."

When they reached it, two men were already set up, their rods in the water.

"Many biting?" he asked, looking at a pail of water where fish, half alive, splattered.

"Good few trout," said one of the fishermen. "No salmon today."

They walked on, enjoying the dappling light from the trees on the tow path.

"Thank you for taking me today," she said.

"It's my pleasure," he said with a smile.

They turned off the canal path, to a field, making their way across tall grasses to the banks of the Boyne. Within minutes of casting out, a tug came on the line and their whoops startled the baby as William reeled the fish in to shore.

It emerged from the water, silver and flipping, the glint of its scales reflecting in the sun.

"A salmon," she said. "A big one too."

"It must be at least ten pounds," he said, weighing it with his hands. "I hope Polly will know what do with it!"

He wrote it into the fishing journal she had bought him.

"You've brought me luck," he said.

"Have I now?" she said and smiled. "I'd imagine it's more to do with those scrumptious disgusting worms wriggling in that bait box."

They both laughed.

When Anna Genevieve started to grizzle, they gathered their things and made their way back to catch the boat again.

"I could be Queen of the Nile," said the Nanny, lying back and closing her eyes as the boat sailed with speed back to the dock at Beauparc.

"You certainly look like a queen," he said.

She sat up, opened her eyes and looked at him.

The sun must be going to his head, he thought. But there they were. He was enjoying himself. And Miss Murphy looked radiant, carrying his daughter, both their faces wrapped in summer smiles.

‿◦�〇◦‿

That evening, they took a light supper, the sun having sent Anna Genevieve to sleep early.

"You have a red nose," she told him at the table.

"Have I?" he said. "Your face is as white as porcelain."

"Yes," she said. "It seems my nose is daintier and doesn't catch the sun as much."

Her joke made him laugh.

He raised his glass.

"To a wonderful day! May there be many more in the future!"

"To the future!" she said, holding her glass in the air.

# CHAPTER 22

## *Mrs. McHugh*

She filled her days with tiny tasks, stretching them out, trying to extend everything to fill up her time. When she'd cleaned over the kitchen after breakfast, she tended to her shopping list. Then she did the floors, the bedroom and any laundry that was drying or needed airing.

She changed her sheets once a week, but with only herself in the bed they were twice as clean. Still, it gave her something to do.

Every day she walked to the grocer's. Not to the one nearest, in George's Street, but to West Street, passing another four grocer's on the way, in the hope she might meet with someone for a chat.

She kept some items over, knowing she could do with a slab of butter or dripping, but keeping it till tomorrow, for the next day's list, to have something on it, to give her something to get up for, to go and get.

Cooking for one was not the same as cooking for two. She didn't have to make a dinner if she didn't want to. She could heat up some tinned beef or fry an egg or just eat bread and cheese if she wanted. But she did try to cook. To give her something to do.

In the afternoons, after she'd been out to the store in the morning, she would go for her walk. She'd go in the opposite direction of the town, out towards Barnattan or Tullyallen or Mell, anywhere the road was long and winding and would take up to an hour to walk.

Her favourite place to go was out along the river, to the canal, to watch the barges making their way from Navan and Slane to Drogheda Port. She loved to see the bustle, the goods being carried out to faraway places. Things being made and grown and produced, to feed and clothe and refresh others. So much life.

She started attending daily morning Mass. She was so used to being up early and to work each day that she needed to have something to get up for, to be somewhere on time.

And after Mass, every morning, she visited Mick's grave. She spoke with him as if he were right there, telling him anything she could think of to say. But with very little news, she found she was prattling on most mornings, talking out loud, about the weather, about her aching back, about what she was planning to cook for her tea.

She noticed she'd lost weight, the band on her skirts feeling looser as the weeks passed. When she looked in the small mirror on the back of the kitchen door, she noticed her face looked leaner, two slight lines appearing on her cheeks.

Mick would have said, *Ah, would you ever stop and go put some meat on your bones!*

Betty would have said, *Sure, couldn't you have done with losing it anyway, Mrs. McHugh? Too many potatoes, that's your problem.*

Her two best friends in the world, gone. All in the space of a few days of each other.

The world could be a cruel, cruel place.

But you had to get on with things, didn't you? Sure, what else could you do?

❧

They'd laid him out in the sitting room, on a kitchen table borrowed from two doors up.

"I just can't get over it," she said to Mrs. Doherty, as they washed and dressed him. Her face was pale from shock.

"God takes when he decides and often the best go first," said Mrs. Doherty comfortingly.

When he was ready and Mrs. Doherty left the room, she put her head on his chest and let the tears fall onto his wool waistcoat. It felt so wrong, feeling his coldness beneath her.

Someone had left a glass of whiskey on the mantelpiece beside Mick's pipe. She took both and sat in his chair. She lit the pipe, sucking on it, coughing as the smoke entered her lungs.

"Look what you've driven me to," she said, taking a gulp of the whiskey which burned her throat. "I'm a different woman now, Mick. I'm a changed woman."

The smell of his pipe was a comfort.

They'd had trouble with the lockjaw and the contortion of his body. She didn't think he looked like himself in the coffin. She sat by him for as long as she could, but seeing his distorted face, his cold skin, it didn't feel real.

How would she get through this without him?

The neighbours were good. They gathered round, seeing to everything, doing practical things like cleaning the house and making tea and bringing in food for the trail of mourners that came.

They brought her tea too and sometimes she managed to take a bit into her mouth and let it go down. But there was no eating. A knot had formed in her stomach. It sat in the middle of her intestines, filling her up with bile, suffocating her throat.

On the third day, the day of the burial, she had managed a nibble of a scone lathered with butter. It felt crumbly in her mouth, but the butter helped it go down, sweeping past her throat, into her stomach of despair.

It quelled the sickness for a while. But soon, the nausea was back and there was nothing she could do to get more food into her. Her hand would not lift to her mouth.

He hadn't suffered long, they said. *Not in the long run.*

But they hadn't seen his eyes, the fright in them as his body convulsed and the fits took over.

It pained her, the life they were supposed to have. They should have had longer, she should have had time to mind him as he aged, time to look back over their lives and remember. They still had trips to Liverpool to take, picnics to eat, walks to go on. Now, he would never accompany her on the steamer again.

She had administered the Fowler's Solution when

176

she'd got back from the chemist's on the Saturday morning, but the pains in his stomach got worse. He vomited continuously, weakened, nothing left in his body to spit out.

Still the waves came.

She went next door to get someone to go for the doctor, who came two hours later. He was an older man who used to attend to her mother. He could see the worry in her as she stood by Mick's bedside, handing him another bowl for him to vomit into.

"It's a bad case of gastroenteritis," he said. "It's been doing the rounds."

He prescribed rhubarb pills and a black draught of senna pods to help clear the bowels.

"I'll visit tomorrow if you like," he said.

"Yes," she said, her face white. "Please come back tomorrow, doctor."

The pills did not stay down but after a while Mick seemed to relax and he lay back in bed and went to sleep.

Later that night, when she was satisfied that he was resting and hoping that the bug might be finally out of his system, she left him to go and make some tea and eat something herself. She hoped she didn't catch the bug too, the two of them struck down, helpless.

As she poured the boiling water into the teapot, a strangled cry came from the bedroom. She raced upstairs and from the bedroom door she saw that Mick was contorting in the bed, convulsions wracking his body.

"*Mick!*" She ran over to him to try and support his head.

"*Can't breathe!*" he gasped.

She watched his chest restrict and his arms and legs

freeze up in the bed, the muscles on his arm hardening beneath her fingers. She tried to pull him up into a sitting position to get some air into his lungs.

He screamed out again, in agony. "I can't get a breath," he said, his words strangling in his throat. His jaw flew back into a horrible locked position.

She left him to run next door, banging on the door and shouting.

"Call the doctor, will you?" she said when her neighbour answered in her nightclothes. "Mick's after taking a turn, he's very bad."

A messenger was sent and the neighbour came into the house, calling first for Mrs. Doherty to see if she could help.

When they got to the room Mick was arched in the bed like a bow, his wife clutching at him.

"*Mick!*" she cried again, trying to cradle his head, but he was shaking so bad that she had to step back from the bed. Tears flowed down her cheeks.

The convulsions went on for twenty minutes and there was nothing they could do to bring them to a halt. A number of other neighbours gathered in the room, but when they went near him it seemed to make the shaking worse and he cried out if anyone touched his skin.

Someone started a decade of the rosary and they stood about the convulsing man, hoping for divine intervention.

At ten past midnight the shaking began to slow and Mick seemed to weaken. He started to go quiet but the convulsions did not stop, his body still twisting and his muscles spasming.

With the quietness, his wife came back to his bedside, her eyes red from crying.

"Mick," she said softly, but his eyes were now closed.

They watched as his chest heaved and then they realised that the shaking had stopped and so had his chest. He was no longer breathing. He had passed, going quiet in the end, his limbs still twisted out of shape, his eyes thrown back in their sockets.

With the realisation of what had happened, his wife let a roar out of her and then a wail and threw herself across his body. The neighbours stood around and rubbed her back, looking at each other with wide eyes, continuing to say the rosary, bleated words over the muffled sobs of a heartbroken woman.

When the doctor arrived, with his cap and cape on, panting from the late-night ride, he went to the bedside, took out his pocket watch and placed two fingers to Mick's silent neck.

"It looks like lockjaw," the doctor said, noting Mick's contorted face. "Tetanus. I really am very sorry."

⁌⁖⁍

On the second night of the wake, there were a few songs in the kitchen in the evening, something to bring the atmosphere up. She tried to join in, but her heart wasn't in it, so she listened and let the tears roll, in between smiling at memories they brought up.

A soft knock came to the front door and Mrs. Doherty poked her head into kitchen, nodding at Mrs. McHugh over the singing.

"William Thomas has come to see you."

The singing stopped for a moment as Mrs. McHugh followed Mrs. Doherty out to the hall.

Mr. Thomas stood in the small corridor, clearing his throat.

"I just heard today," he said. "I am so sorry."

She looked at him and smiled sadly.

"He's in here," she said, walking past him to lead him into the sitting room where Mick was laid out. The mourners who were in the room, clutching cups of tea and glasses of spirits, got up and left to give them some privacy.

"Poor Mick," she said.

"Yes," he said. "What a shock for you."

"It's the weekend for it," she said wryly.

He cleared his throat again. "I'm sorry about that too, about what happened."

"As am I," she said.

A silence hung in the room, neither wishing to discuss the issue in the presence of the deceased man.

"How is Anna Genevieve, is she well?" she said finally.

"She is well."

"I miss her."

"I will be at the funeral," he said, "and if there is anything you need, anything at all, please don't hesitate to ask."

She bowed her head.

William cleared his throat again and turned to leave.

"You know, he was very upset," she said. "Before he got sick. We both were, we were both sick to the stomach. Over what happened."

"I'm sorry," William muttered, almost inaudibly.

"They were his last memories – of me, dreadfully upset."

He sighed and went to say something but thought better of it. Instead, he bowed his head and left the room.

Outside the cottage he stood on the road for a moment, to gather his breath. He looked up at the night sky and closed his eyes. It was hard to shake the feeling that somehow, in all this mess, he had made a terrible mistake somewhere along the way.

⥀⥂⥀

"What did *he* want?" asked Susan.

"To offer his condolences," said Mrs. McHugh, pursing her lips.

"Bastard!" said Susan, to a few positive murmurs in support.

Susan had come from Kells as soon as she had heard about her brother-in-law's death, bringing her husband and daughter Catherine with her. They were staying in the good spare room upstairs and, along with Mrs. Doherty, had taken over most of the responsibilities for the funeral.

"Have we any more mustard?" Susan asked loudly, looking over at Mrs. Doherty from her place at the table where she was buttering bread and making cheese and ham sandwiches.

"I can get some from home," said Mrs. Doherty, rising to go.

Mrs. McHugh watched her sister walk over and put the empty mustard jar in the basket where glasses were being stacked.

There'd be no more mustard in the house now with Mick gone.

Mrs. McHugh burst into tears, causing Susan to stop what she was doing and go to put her arms around her sister.

"There, there, pet," she said. "It'll be all right. I promise. It'll be all right."

⥀⥂⥀

"Why don't you come and stay with me? I think you'd like it," said Susan as they sat, the day after the funeral, nursing a cup of tea in front of the fire.

With the funeral over, Mrs. McHugh was finding she was able to eat and drink a little more, the anguish along with the press of people somewhat dissipated. She realised she was very weak from the trauma and lack of nourishment over the past few days.

"Ah sure, what would I want with in Kells?"

"The company. And there's plenty of work, to keep you occupied."

"Amn't I retired now?"

"There's still life in you yet."

"It's too late for that. This is my home. I'd never leave this house."

"No, I suppose not," said Susan, and she looked around the small sitting room where they'd been raised. "Hard to believe we were all brought up in here, isn't it?"

"I always thought I'd raise children of my own here," said Mrs. McHugh sadly. "But, sure, it wasn't to be."

"No," said Susan.

They were silent for a moment, each slurping from their cup of dark tea.

"It's bringing back a lot of memories, being back," said Susan.

"Aye," said Mrs. McHugh. "Your old bedroom will do that to you."

"Do you ever think about him?" asked Susan, and she looked directly at her sister, her face like stone.

"No," she said. "Never."

"I thought he might turn up here, this weekend."

"And how would that happen?" asked Mrs McHugh, smartly.

"Winnie ... it's ten years now."

Mrs. McHugh looked away angrily.

"I don't want to talk about him."

"We don't know where he'll go yet, whether he'll come back here or ..."

"I said I don't want to talk about him."

They were silent again, her snap setting an atmosphere amid the crackle of the fire.

"Think about coming to Kells for a while. We'd love to have you. All the grandchildren are only dying to get to know their old aunt better."

"Old!" she said.

"You know what I mean. Even if you were still working, I wouldn't be feeling so bad about you."

"Yes ... well ..." she sniffed, "never mind that. I'll think about it but, to be honest, traipsing across the country wouldn't suit me, Susan. This is my new lot and I'm going to have to get used to it."

"Yes," said Susan. "I suppose so."

In all the fuss, in all the commotion, between the birth of Anna Genevieve, the death of Mrs. Thomas, the arrival of the Nanny and what had happened since, she had completely forgotten about the ten-year anniversary and what it meant.

That his time was up and he would be back out.

And now she didn't even have Mick to protect her.

# CHAPTER 23

*Christy*

The hansom cab was a thing of beauty. He took pride in waxing it up, in rubbing the glass with newspaper to give it that polished finish. The novelty had yet to wear off sailing round the city, perched high, watching the horse's legs clip-clop across the bridges, cobbles and smooth roads of the southside.

He'd had to learn the streets by heart, about where was best to turn and where the good stations were, for water, for waiting, for the tipping fares.

He'd often drive out to the zoo and to Phoenix Park to take day trippers back into the city. On warm days he'd ferry passengers out towards Kingstown, doing short trips all day, but mostly it was businessmen and city workers he taxied about in the small, swift cab.

He worked the day shifts mainly and, when he returned to the stables, he would take the wiping cloth and go over the carriage, puffing on the glass to take away the finger-marks, checking it over for any damages or scrapes.

It had been easy to go from stable hand to cabbie. He knew they wouldn't keep a man like him doing a boy's job – shovelling shit all day, fetching hay and straw, hawking bags of oats around.

He was too presentable, too charming. He was wasted in the stables.

When a cabbie came down with dysentery, the headman asked him if he could help out with the busy lunch hour, to take the cab out for the rush.

"See how you get on," he said.

He got on very well. He could handle the horse. He feigned confidence, seated up high, controlling the cab. If he didn't know the exact street they were heading to, he asked the customer if they could guide him, explaining that he was new to the job, and that he'd be ever so grateful if they could assist.

He helped out all that week, studying the maps as he waited for fares, chatting with other drivers, picking up all the tips they offered and being very forthcoming about how nervous he was being a first-time cabbie.

He wasn't nervous at all, but he knew he would seem less of a threat by being endearing.

This, he had learned.

She'd sent a telegram to say that it was done. He smiled and let the paper and envelope flitter down beside his breakfast of greasy sausages and black pudding.

*Job done. He suffered in the end. Heard she was in a bad way. Hoping this pleases you, sir?*

He laughed out loud. Old prick Mick, standing with his arms around Winnie, shielding her in court that day.

Well, she was alone now.

You couldn't betray your own flesh and blood like that and get away with it.

The news put him in a buoyant mood.

The lodgings he had now were much more to his liking. Nothing fancy, nothing to be too proud of, but they were private and his own. He liked that it was on the flat, that there were no stairs to climb and that it was tucked away, nice and neat, not too far from all the train and cab stations, the southside within walking distance.

He got out to the southside as much as he could, taking off over the bridge to look at the big houses and their shiny brass doorknobs and gleaming steps, washed by the hands of a thousand housemaids.

The freedom, the pure joy he felt at being able to go and do whatever he wanted at whatever time of day, still had not subsided. He wondered if it ever would.

There were things he missed about the Joy though. He missed the banter. In the evenings, the stillness got to him.

When that happened, he'd put a few coins in his pocket and make his way over to the Monto. Now that he was getting to know who was who, he had some regulars he liked, but it was always a thrill to get a look at someone new. Especially the younger ones, the innocent ones, with fright in their eyes.

He always liked to find one of them.

Maggie had been on at him to come and visit. She wanted to see him, desperate now that he was out.

He didn't want to see her yet. He felt as though he needed some time to adjust, some time by himself. The woman had an awful crowding way about her.

He liked the peace and quiet. The time to think. Even if it was a bit lonely.

Maggie brought her own troubles with her. Always did. Always would.

⁓⊙⊙⁓

He knew she was trouble the very day he laid eyes on her. He caught her staring at him, out from under that white workhouse cap. She looked at him and stuck out her lip and blew a bit of hair up over her eye, real gamey she was.

"What are you looking at?" he said, seeing what her reaction would be.

"You."

Cheeky mare.

And asking for a cigarette. Real brazen. He should have known from the set of her to keep away.

The other lads told him that those workhouse women were nothing but bad news. But he couldn't help it, he liked her, there was something about her that drew him.

It was during one of their embraces, when he was up real close to her and he wanted to take her, there and then, that he told her about his cottage. Not too far from the workhouse at all. Just up the road. If she could get out at all ...

He didn't actually think she'd find the way to get out, with all the doors closed and barred at night. But that was Maggie. That was Maggie all over.

"There are two big stones," she told him. "They're loose – in the back wall. I noticed them up by the yew tree last week when I was playing hide and seek with Kitty. It's like someone tried to escape before. I tried to pull them out, but they wouldn't come all the way. If they came out, I could squeeze through the hole. If you go and knock them out, with a chisel, just chip away at them and put them back, then I'd be able to use them. Like a door."

She looked at him, up out of those dark-blue eyes, blinking.

"All right," he told her, and that evening just before it got dark, he took his chisel and a little hammer and he found the stones, right behind the yew tree, like she told him. He chipped away until they came loose in his hands, the top one first, and then he put them back.

"It's done," he told her the next day, in between loading a cart of starch boxes.

And that was it. The escape artist, his little night-time visitor, standing at the door that very evening and he about to sit down to his spuds.

Red-faced from running. Panting. Wanting him.

He took her in of course and fed her. She was like a starving cat. She ate half his food, munching on the sausages like she'd never tasted meat before.

And when she was fed she was ready for him. Mad for him she was. Couldn't get enough, all kissing and stroking him and wanting more.

Of course, he went with it, his body responding like any man's would. But even then, he knew. That she was dangerous.

When it was done, when she lay there, spent, snuggled into him, telling him how she wished she could stay the night, he remembered another woman, older – her name was Maggie too.

He'd even been with her once, when he'd come out of the pub pissed, and she was there, hunching her dress up to reveal a milky-white thigh.

He couldn't help himself. Whenever any woman was forward like that, it did something, it moved him inside.

So, he'd gone with her, drunk, and she'd taken him back to the little rundown house she was shacked up in. Not that he cared. Mad Maggie was what she was, a whore, offering a good time, if you were drunk enough to go with it.

When it was done and she was fixing herself, he leaned against the wall, smoking a cigarette, and he realised there was a ragged curtain, hanging across the bedroom.

Out of the corner of his eye he caught a movement, like a little cat, moving behind the material.

A girl. He saw her peeping out, their eyes locked for a second and he said to Maggie, "Is that your little girl?

She laughed. "Don't mind them, they're asleep anyway. They get a good dose of soothing syrup every night, sleep like babies they do."

But one of them was awake. He'd seen her and she'd seen him.

And he'd forgotten about that, didn't even ever think of it, until now.

"What was your ma's name?" he said, his mouth muffled in her hair.

"Margaret, like me," she said. "Why?"

She pushed up on her elbows, glaring.

"No reason," he said and smiled at her.

Like mother like daughter. The two Maggies.

Bitch of a whore.

Trouble.

He hated her relying on him.

He should have told her all the way back then, when she first started calling to the cottage, to be away with herself. To leave him alone, to head back to the workhouse like a good little girl and forget all the notions she had about him.

Even the aul' fella next door started to notice.

"Saw you had a lady visitor last night," he said one morning to him.

"Mind your own fucking business," he told him, straight off.

He had to get Maggie to calm a bit. He had to let her know that it wasn't on to be calling so much.

"The man next door," he told her. "He saw you. You need to be careful. I don't think calling nearly every night is a good idea."

"What do you mean?" she said, her eyes flashing dangerously.

"Well, I'm just saying, if you get caught you'll get in trouble and if I get caught ... I don't want to lose my job, Maggie."

"So what?" she said. "You could get another."

"Maggie," he said, pleadingly.

"Are you telling me you don't want me calling any more?"

"It's not that," he said. "I'm worried it won't end well."

"The only way it won't end well is if you betray me, Christy McCoy," she said, glowering.

He felt trapped. Fucking Maggie.

He thought about sealing up the stones in the wall, setting them in plaster, something to end this affair that was getting far too serious.

He thought about skipping it for a while, taking off to Dublin.

But then he had another idea, something that would see her step back, take a break maybe.

He was sorry the way it happened, in the end, with

the timing and all. He never meant for it to happen like that.

But it did give her the chance to escape, to get her head straight.

Well, as straight as any head could be on a girl like that.

# CHAPTER 24

*The Nanny*

She knew Kitty couldn't remember the before. Not really. She had some memories but it was hard to tell what were her own thoughts and what were the thoughts she had placed there for her, telling her only the good things about their mother.

Because there were good things. She had to search for them and, truth be told, she had to make a lot of them up, but what else could you do with a little girl who didn't remember her mother?

It was easy to paint a picture of someone when they were gone. She could say anything she wanted, tell her their mother was beautiful and caring and giving and there was nothing Kitty could do but believe her. It wasn't like she was going to show up there and reveal to everyone that she wasn't beautiful, caring and loving after all.

That her jaws were so sunken, on account of the teeth that had been punched from her gums, that it made her large nose even more prominent. That her dark eyebrows almost met in the middle, that if you squinted sometimes she really did have the look of a witch about her.

It hadn't always been like that. She remembered her mother from when she was small, and she didn't look haggard or tired or witchlike at all.

She looked strong. Handsome even. But that was before.

Before the drink and the snuff and the not eating for days and the being outside, exposed to the elements. Before the men who had taken her and left her bruised, battered and scarred. Before the men who broke her cheekbones and her nose and even the ears in her head, crushing the cartilage, biting and nearly pulling them from her scalp.

No, she hadn't always looked like that.

She knew now, when she looked in the speckled mirror at Number 43, that there was a look of her mother about her. It had brought it all back, coming to this town – stirring up memories, reminding her of where she had come from, who she was.

She'd inherited her mother's large nose and heavy brow, but she had a different mouth. A kinder mouth. It made her better-looking. Maybe she had the same mouth as her father. Whatever her father had looked like. She used to search the faces of the men that came to the house, the ones they met on the street, always scrutinising them to see if one of them looked like her.

Her mother said her father was a sailor. But what was truth and what was lies?

"Tell me about Mama."

Every night. Before they went to sleep, laid out in their narrow workhouse beds, they'd whisper.

"Mama is a great beauty," she would tell Kitty. "She has dark hair, as black as a raven's and a mouth as red as a rose. And she was so happy when you came along that we celebrated with tea and biscuits and after that she said she was the happiest Mama there ever was."

"Will I see her again?"

"I don't know, lovey. You might. And, if you don't, I'll always be here to mind you."

It made her feel better, telling the child these fibs, making up stories so that she never knew the truth. Of where she'd come from. Of who she was.

Soon though, the other children would tell her. You couldn't live in a place like this and be protected. She was waiting for the question that would inevitably one day come: *Maggie, what is a whore?*

And what could she say to that?

❧

She had tried to stay in the rented rooms where they'd been living, in a cold shell of a building. But the authorities were on to them. She shunted the kitchen table right up against the door and barricaded them in. When it was discovered that their mother was gone, that she'd been taken to prison, then that was the end.

The police came. The neighbours stood round. A thirteen-year-old and a three-year-old. Left to fend for themselves.

To the workhouse it was.

As they walked there, escorted by a policeman who knew them well, who had often told them when he found them standing out in the cold, to go on home, to get into bed and wrap themselves in their blankets, even though they had no blankets at all, part of her felt relief.

At the workhouse there would be shelter. Stirabout. Maybe even some meat on Sundays. A dry bed, with a blanket. They wouldn't have to worry at night, about who would be coming into their bedroom, about what state their mother would be in and whether she'd be home at all.

They knew exactly where she was now.

As they walked up the steep hill towards the workhouse, she fondly stroked Kitty's hair, tied neatly back with the yellow ribbon, her most precious possession in the world.

There would be no whoring any more, not for them. There would be no drinking and carousing and going the way their mother did.

She would look after her sister and she would look after herself and, as soon as she was old enough, she would leave that workhouse and get the two of them settled into a new life.

She took Kitty's hand as the policeman pulled back the knocker on the great wooden door of Drogheda Union Workhouse. It trembled in her palm, like a trapped butterfly on a hot summer's day.

꧁ꙮ꧂

They were given new shoes when they arrived, small boots for Kitty and tough boots for her that didn't even look like they'd been worn that often before. They felt heavy on her feet.

For the first few nights, when the lights went out, Kitty climbed from her bed into hers, creeping under the blanket, wrapping her tiny body around her, as they had always done, as they had always slept.

But with her full belly and all the play during the day, soon she was so tired in the evenings that she fell asleep in her own bed and forgot to climb into hers.

It was a good sign, she thought. Things were improving.

She was assigned to the laundry, where she marvelled at the vast vats of boiling water, mangles and ironing boards.

The room was filled with steam and the scent of detergent and water.

It was hot and heavy work and her brow dripped with the exertion as they swirled sheets and pinafores and cottons. Kitty went to the schoolhouse with the other children. When she was older, she too would be placed in the laundry, to help sort and starch.

Things were better at the workhouse. With segregation, there were no men coming and going. Protecting Kitty had always been her priority, and even though her mother had let some of the men into their bed, some that paid for it while she looked the other way and some that snuck in when their mother was passed out, she had never once let them touch Kitty.

Even though some of the dirty bastards wanted to.

There had been no one stopping them, though, when she herself was that age.

One day, the master of the workhouse, Mr. McGovern stood up at dinnertime, cracking a stick on the table. The room fell silent, waiting to hear him speak.

"Opportunities have arisen for girls that would like to

train in domestic service," he said. "We have a number of good families willing to take you on. You can come to my office tomorrow, to see me."

And with that he sat down.

All night she thought about what the master had said.

Training in domestic service would give her a head start. The laundry was backbreaking work. In a house, she would receive a wage, board and learn new skills, skills that would see her acceptable and employable, anywhere in Ireland.

A host of girls stood outside the master's office the following morning.

They were silent, on edge, shuffling and clearing their throats, waiting to be called.

She was left to last, the master overlooking her, not calling her name, even though she had been there well before some other girls.

When he called her into his office, she felt annoyed to have been left till last.

"Margaret," he said and he sat back in his chair, showing off his belly, which was round and hard and popped a little over his trousers.

She stood in front of him, bowing her head.

"I would like to put us forward for domestic service, sir," she said. "Myself and Kitty. We are hard workers – we would do our best, sir."

"Would you now?" he said and smiled.

She didn't like the smile. She recognised it. It was a smile that wasn't really a smile at all. A smile full of badness.

"And what makes you think we would find a home for you two girls?"

"You said there were opportunities, sir."

"Yes, opportunities for *decent* girls," he said.

He leaned back even further so that the buttonhole stretched on his trousers.

"What skills do you think you could bring, domestically?" he said.

"We are hard workers, sir. I have the laundry experience. I can cook a bit."

She racked her brains. She couldn't sew. Truth be told, she could barely cook either, but she needed to sell herself.

"I can light a fire from nothing, sir," she said.

It didn't look at though her words were impressing him.

He stood up, his chair scratching on the wooden floor.

"What makes you think a decent family would have you?"

He had walked around his desk and was now standing over her.

"I ..."

He smelled clean, a scent of soap lingering in the air around him. She noticed his sideburns, which had been neatly shorn with a razor.

"Do you really think we're going to send two little whores out for domestic service? Do you think anyone around here would want anything to do with you two dirty little bitches?"

His face was next to hers and she could smell his breath now, sour, compared to the soap.

She stood, unable to move and stared at the ground, afraid to raise her eyes to his face.

*"Get out of my sight!"*

Well, there it was. There was the truth. They could come to the workhouse, they could do their best, but nothing would ever change.

They were their mother's daughters.

Raised in a workhouse and no future at the end of it.

Well, she'd show him, if it was the last thing she did. She was going to make a life for herself, for them. Whatever it took, whatever she had to do.

Nothing was going to get in her way.

Of that, she was sure.

# CHAPTER 25

## William D. Thomas

"Margaret, how would you feel about attending a function with me? It's in the Whitworth, this Saturday."

She smiled, delicately. "I would be honoured."

"If you need to arrange for something to wear, you'll find a pound note in the pot on the sideboard. Please take it to organise whatever you may need."

"That's most kind."

"I'm not a fan of these functions, but it's the summer ball and I feel it's bad for business if I don't attend."

She smiled daintily again.

William was pleased. It would be so much more pleasant attending the dinner dance with Margaret on his arm, than on his own. She would be a distraction among the small talk and dealing with all the well-intentioned questions people asked of a grieving husband.

He was quite taken aback when Margaret came down the stairs on Saturday evening, wearing a tight-corseted dress, which sat below the upper curves of her bosom. Silk gloves stretched to her elbows. He bowed a little in greeting and told her she looked wonderful.

It was not a lie.

He wanted to take her hand and kiss it, but he couldn't quite bring himself to do it. He would see how the evening panned out. Tonight was a test.

They walked the short distance to the handsome redbrick Whitworth Hall. It stretched into the sky, grey arched windows and doors yawning in its façade. He felt her hold her breath as they mounted the steps, which were crowded with other guests. Carriages were pulling up and letting their passengers out and quite a queue had formed. Some of the carriages turned, causing a traffic jam, while others waited to pass under St Laurence's Gate, the medieval barbican tower, one at a time.

The Whitworth was where he had first danced with Anna, all those years ago at Christmas time. He felt a stab of longing, wishing that he was climbing the steps, about to meet her and dance with her for the first time, all over again.

They were greeted by the ball organisers, Mr. Coddington and his wife who considered herself something of a socialite. Coddington chaired the Chamber of Commerce and, while he was busy attending meetings on rates and taxes, the glamourous Mrs. C organised large balls, dances and race trips.

"W. D. Thomas, how wonderful to see you," said Mr.

Coddington. "You are most welcome, most welcome."

Mrs. Coddington had a great big hostess smile painted on her face.

"Miss Margaret Murphy," William said, introducing his companion.

Margaret was gracious in her greeting, dipping her knee in a curtsy and smiling.

"Have you been to the Whitworth before?" asked Mrs. Coddington.

"This is my first time," she said.

"How exciting for you. Do fetch yourself a drink. And enjoy your night."

He felt the Coddingtons close in to each other and whisper as he and Margaret walked away, a communication that they had just witnessed something very worthy of party conversation. William D. Thomas with a new lady on his arm.

Inside, the atmosphere was already building. Soft gas lighting lit up the room and the faces of the guests. The room was full, with women dressed in fine silk dresses, some with furs, others with pearls and diamonds. Chatter filled the air and the clink of glasses, grabbed from trays floating past made-up faces, pierced the din.

He got Margaret a sweet champagne.

"This is ever so elegant," she said, her eyes darting around the room.

Until now, he had not even thought about what an overwhelming experience this might be for her. He hadn't really thought too much about the dance at all, other than that he would go and that he wanted to get speaking to the harbour master at some point about the new quay being planned at the port.

"Have you ever been at a function like this before?" he asked.

"No," she whispered.

"Right," he said. "Sip the drinks. Lots of them. They'll help. Smile. At everyone. If someone is being a total bore, excuse yourself to the ladies' room. And you will have to dance with me, later. It's expected." He smiled. "We should try to enjoy ourselves."

"Yes," she said. "Thank you for inviting me. I feel quite lucky to be here."

"You won't be saying that after Mrs. Mac is done with you."

She looked up to see an old lady with grey hair, her large crinoline sweeping the floor, making a beeline for them both.

"*Mr. Thomas!*" she shouted from a few feet away. "And who is your lady friend? My, it's good to see you back out and about – you are looking so fresh – I'm *delighted* to see you."

The woman held her drink in the air as she fired question after question, nodding feverishly, draining as much information as she could.

How was the baby doing? How was he doing after the loss of his wife? How was business? Any plans for expansion? And who was this lovely lady and where did she come from?

"I am caring for the baby," Margaret answered. "I have come to assist Mr. Thomas."

"Are you a nursemaid?" asked the old lady.

"She's a little more than that," said Mr. Thomas.

The old lady sucked in her breath.

"I suppose a small baby needs a mother," she said, glaring.

The band struck up and he used it as a cue to excuse them both. He took Margaret by the hand and led her around the room in a lively two-step.

"The Inquisition," he said in her ear.

"She was very curious," she said.

"Expect more of that," he said. "These women have nothing better to do, than gossip."

Margaret was unsure about dancing. He could feel her concentration as she gripped him by the elbow, her feet grappling with the floor.

"Just look up and hang on," he whispered, helping her and smiling.

After another two step they went to get another drink and he managed to lead them to a group of businessmen involved in the port. The men were investors who wanted to build the second dock, some with large shipping companies, exporters and importers, marine men who made decisions that affected all of their livelihoods. Soon he was sucked into their conversation and Margaret smiled and sipped her drink, as dutiful as any longstanding wife.

When the canapés were gone, when they'd danced some more, when the first drunks were beginning to bump their way around the room, and when he was happy that he had made his impression on the appropriate business associates, they left.

"We do hope to see you again, Miss Murphy," said Mrs. Coddington, as they bid their goodbyes.

He found it a little amusing. They would see her pushing the perambulator tomorrow if they so wished to watch the street.

They swayed against each other gently as they made their way down Laurence Street, making the short journey last as long as possible.

"Let's walk down to the river for some air," he suggested.

They walked down Shop Street and came to the

bridge, turning left to walk along the docks down towards his offices. Two ships, their ropes springing at all angles from the sails were docked at the low wall, their gangplanks hung across the gap.

"That was such an enjoyable evening," she said. "It felt most special. I'm really not used to such pleasures. Drinking alcohol. Dancing."

"You should get used to it," said William. "I'm quite an expert in drinking and dancing."

She laughed.

"I know it might be frowned upon," he said. "I'm aware that there are people who object to me stepping out with you. But I enjoy your company. And I have been quite lonely these past few months."

He was talking as if practising a speech, giving reasons why their friendship should be accepted.

"I am glad that I have been able to help a little," she said.

"You've helped more than a little," he said, turning to her. He took her gloved hands in his. "You have brightened my evenings. I look forward to coming home to you each day. And it means so much to me that Anna Genevieve is being looked after, in your care."

He leaned in and kissed her gently on the lips, letting the kiss linger in the dark dusk along the quays.

She pulled back, smiling.

"You are a very fine man, Mr. Thomas," she said.

"Let's go home," he said and they walked hand in hand, back up Shop Street, past a man sweeping the road, past the carriages sailing up to Whitworth to collect their passengers, past the Tholsel as the clock struck fifteen minutes past midnight, all the way back to Number 43, Laurence Street.

# CHAPTER 26

## The Investigation

"I told you," she said angrily. "I told you something wasn't right. And you laughed at me and said I was away with the fairies and an awful woman, but wasn't I right? Two babies! Buried in our garden!"

The woman had her arms folded across her body, and she stood staring out the kitchen window, her eyes on the spades, where a robin was hopping about.

"The poor loves," she said. "The poor little things."

He came and wrapped his arms around her and at first she pushed him away but he persisted and they stood there, in an embrace, waiting for the policeman.

"What did she do to them?" she said. "That woman, what did she do to them?"

She turned her face to him, pleading.

"I don't know, love," he said. "I don't know."

They had fled to the kitchen, slamming the back door hard, standing as far back as possible in the room, to try and distance themselves from the horror that lay outside.

He had gone out the front door to the woman down the road, rapping on her window, asking her to fetch the police.

Within the hour, while they still waited for the policeman, all the households within proximity had gathered at their house, crowding into the kitchen, offering their condolences, letting the family know if there was anything they could do, to just ask, anything at all.

It was a strange atmosphere, all these people coming to sympathise, when they hadn't met most of them yet and the deceased were not theirs.

The policeman ordered everyone to leave while he looked over the scene and interviewed the family. Anyone passing by the house was drawn by the crowd outside and did not move on.

"And she left no new address?"

The policeman was writing, the hair on his hands as dark as the moustache covering his lips. His hand moved deftly over the page of the small notebook, flicking with the scratch of his pen.

"She did not."

"Did you use a solicitor?"

"The sale was direct, sir," said the man. "She was eager to sell."

"Do you have a bank account, a bank that she dealt with?"

The man shook his head.

His wife nudged him, her elbow to his ribs. She wanted him to divulge what she had been complaining about all along. The unnatural atmosphere. The sadness in the house. The utter terror and sense of suffocation she felt at night.

But what could the man say about feelings? How could he tell this policeman, who didn't seem to have a head for nonsense, that his wife had known from the day they moved into this house that there was something wrong?

That for the four months since they'd been here, she'd woken every night, her hands around her throat, feeling she was being strangled?

"All I know is that she said she was going to family up north. And I dropped her off at the train station. We gave her a lift on our cart."

"I'll have to call the coroner," said the policeman. "This is an inquest job."

"How long will that take?" asked the man, wanting to get the bodies out of the ground as quickly as possible.

"Could be today, could be tomorrow."

The two men went back outside. With the man's permission, the policeman took a damp bedsheet from the washing line and draped it over the dig site. They weighed it down with stones along the edges.

The man bent his head, made the Sign of the Cross and mumbled a prayer to himself.

When they got back to the house, the woman whose door he had knocked on was sitting at the kitchen table with her husband.

"James was a lovely fella," said the husband, two long sideburns moving as he talked. "So genuine. A nicer man you couldn't meet. It was a shock when he died. And him not long remarried at all."

"Wanted a mother for those little ones," said the woman, talking over her husband. "I don't know where she came from, he just appeared with her. A thin woman, a bit prim. Well, they were married and that was that. Sure we barely saw him after that. You'd knock at the door and it wouldn't be answered. And only a few weeks later, he had passed as well ... I couldn't believe it. And it was a quick funeral, no proper wake or anything. He was brought to the church and in the ground before we knew it, and she had the twins, holding both of them at Mass and I felt sorry for her. Imagine, I thought, there she is now left with two bairns that aren't even her own and the husband gone."

"She told me they'd died of scarlet fever," said the man. "When she showed me round the house, she said it took both of them in a day."

"Scarlet fever me arse," said the woman.

Her husband told her to shush.

"Well, it is very suspicious," said the woman. "I mean why not have them buried in the graveyard, even if it was scarlet fever?"

She let the question hang in the air. Then another knock sounded on the door, more neighbours wanting to come in now.

"Would you have any idea where the widow might be now?" asked the policeman.

"Not a clue," said the woman.

The policeman left to summon the coroner and then a type of wake began, with well-wishers and callers bringing homemade lemonades and baked dishes and the kettle bubbling over to supply tea to everyone who wanted to come down to the house where the babies had been found buried in the garden.

The children were in their element. As neighbouring children arrived, more small boots were marched upstairs to the back bedroom, which offered a bird's eye view of the sheet under which the babies lay.

"I found them," said Aidan proudly.

The noise and the atmosphere reminded the man and woman of life in the tenements and they found it all quite familiar, having so many kindly faces around.

Word came that the coroner would arrive that evening and if he deemed an inquest necessary, it would be held there in their house. A doctor would be coming along with the coroner to carry out the autopsies and a jury of twelve men would be assembled.

They set about clearing out the scullery, which was, they felt, the most suitable place for an inquest. And while they waited into the bright summer evening, they talked and drank and there was even a song or two, to aid the two little souls on their way to heaven.

❧

The evening sun had almost set when the coroner arrived. The spades from earlier still stood to attention in the soil, the clay now dried around them.

"Have you a handcart?" asked the coroner, looking up from where he was crouched, surveying the scene.

"There's one in the shed."

The policeman and the man walked to the lean-to attached to the house. It was cool inside and a murky scent of must emanated from the buckets, lumps of wood and plant pots stacked messily inside.

The man pulled the small flat handcart from its resting spot in the middle of the shed. It was a useful little item to have in the garden. He'd been delighted to find the woman had left the shed full of practical gardening tools.

Now, as he gave the little cart to the policeman, he realised that she had likely been running away, aided in no small part by him. How could he have been so foolish?

With guidance from the coroner, the policeman lifted the unearthed suitcase from the ground onto the cart.

"Ready?" the coroner asked.

"Ready," he said.

Leading the procession, the policeman wheeled the cart around the side of the house and into the scullery.

As they passed by the kitchen window that overlooked the garden, a flock of hands went up, making the Sign of the Cross at foreheads, mouths and hearts.

The doctor who would perform the autopsy stood beside his tools, laid out on a green sheet of calico. It pained the man to see such torturous-looking instruments in his house.

All around the doctor stood twelve men, the jury who had been sworn in by the coroner. They jostled politely in the confines of the scullery, straining to get a good view of the dissection table. When the policeman lifted the suitcase onto the table, a low murmur filled the room.

He would burn the table when all this was finished with.

When the suitcase was opened again, the smell filled the crowded room. He feared the stench would enter the walls and never leave it.

How had such a wonderful morning turned into this horror show this evening?

He wanted to ask if he could leave but felt that he should stay. Instead he averted his eyes as the doctor set to work, removing the bodies from their case, setting them out on the table, and examining what he could of their remains.

In particular the doctor examined the throats and the bones of the neck. He dictated notes, which the coroner wrote down.

The bodies were badly decomposed. Taking a jar, the doctor lifted tissues from the infants and dropped them into it. He sealed the jars with pig-gut and wrapped them in brown paper.

*Tissues from stomach and intestinal area removed for chemical testing.*

With the bodies so small, the autopsies did not take long.

When the doctor was finished, the undertaker brought in two small wooden coffins and removed the bodies to the kitchen, where they would be waked until burial Mass at the church.

"What is your opinion, doctor?" asked the coroner.

"It is impossible to tell," he said. "The chemical testing will be able to tell us more. The cracked vertebrae could indicate strangulation. But I would prefer to see the results of the testing first. I cannot give a verdict until that comes back."

The men of the jury nodded.

The coroner announced to the jury that a new court date would be set once the results were back and the doctor was able to give his opinion as to the cause of death. He thanked them for their service, at such short notice.

When the jury had filed out of the scullery into the kitchen, for tea and something stronger if they wanted it, the man waited with the coroner, doctor and policeman.

"Do you think we should apply to the board?" asked the doctor, looking at the coroner.

"I do," he said. "We could exhume ahead of the twins going into the grave."

"I will be available," said the doctor.

"Very well," said the coroner. "I'll make the necessary arrangements."

The policeman looked at the man.

The man looked back, his eyes wide, in question.

"James Martin," said the policeman. "We will look to exhume his body."

The man shrugged. So this whole thing would continue.

He hoped they didn't intend to carry out the post-mortem of James Martin in the house too. His wife wouldn't stand for it.

He went to the kitchen where the two miniature coffins were laid out on the large table.

"Lord have mercy on their souls," said his wife, placing her rosary beads across the coffin nearest to her, the only form of comfort she could give to them. And herself.

❧

It all made sense now. She should have trusted her instincts the day she set foot in the place. All those bad dreams. The spirits of those babies, floating around their heads.

She was sick to her stomach about what happened to them. That all this time they were going about their business and those two little babies lay cold in the garden. And they were going to grow potatoes on them!

"We can't stay here," she told him later, holding a cooling cup of tea.

"My love," he said, "I know, it's a terrible shock."

"We can't stay here," she repeated. "It's not right."

"Maybe you could go and stay with your sister for a while?"

"No, I mean for good," she said.

He was quiet, then he shook his head. "This is our home now. We won't be leaving."

She looked away, silent and angry.

The neighbours took pleasure in telling them all about the strange goings-on in the house, before they'd bought it. That James Martin had lived in the house all his life, that he had a lovely soft wife who gave birth to twins only to catch puerperal fever and die just a few days later.

And then the woman appeared on the scene, a family friend, he said, and they were married within weeks.

"Far too quick to be natural," said one woman.

"I never liked her," said another.

They saw to it that Aidan was all right, checking to see if he was upset or tearful. The excitement hadn't worn off. He sat in the sitting room, crumbs on a plate in front of him, his sisters surrounding him, chattering in high-pitched tones, ecstatic at the morbid excitement introduced to their home.

But she worried about his dreams, about the minutes before he dropped off to sleep, about the visions that would surely come.

Of course, they'd all seen tragic things in their lives. People pulled under carts in front of them. Husbands kicking wives downstairs at night, other babies who caught the fever and died. There was no point nancying the boy either.

She was so tired. Tired from the shock, tired from the hordes of strangers gathered in their kitchen, tired from the talk of what had been found in their garden, of the widow woman, of where she might be now.

Eventually she had to get himself to stand up and tell everyone they'd be retiring to bed now, that it had been a long day and there was still the funeral to come.

She waited until he was ready to climb the stairs with her. Tonight, of all nights, was not a night to be going to bed alone.

She kept the candle burning by the bedside, watching the ceiling where she felt the dark swirls moved.

"I'm sorry," he said, turning to look at her, his head on the pillow.

She continued to stare at the ceiling.

A tear ran down her face, diving onto the pillow.

"You have brought this on us," she said.

Her voice was low and cold. It sent a chill through him.

"This is your doing. Your dream. Your country life and look what it's brought. You can stay here if you wish. I'm not staying in a haunted house. Where a woman could do that to two innocent souls. They're watching us at night. They're still here. Stuck between two worlds."

She turned over in the bed with force, shaking the mattress, the headboard rattling.

"My love," he said, and he grabbed her by the elbow, "we'll get the priest in, get the house blessed."

"It's too late for that. It'll take more than a priest."

"What'll it take?"

"Find that woman," she said. "And have her hung."

# CHAPTER 27

## *The Betrayal*

He picked a nice blonde one, a good bit older, sophisticated. She had a good big rack too, the opposite of Maggie.

He'd been watching the Dublin Road, keeping an eye to see who was going up and down. He knew a lot of the women to see, just like he'd known Maggie's mother to see. But this one was new, seemed to have come down from the North to work for a while – she had a northern twang on her, Dundalk or Newry maybe.

He didn't tell her what he was doing, just that he wanted her to come back to his cottage for the evening, that he wanted the company and a bit of fun. He told her he'd pay her extra for the hours she wasn't out on the street and she was agreeable to this.

Being paid to be in out of the cold was all right by her.

Her blonde hair was scraped back from her face, greasy, black roots showing. The lines on her face were ingrained into the skin, from years standing on the streets.

He'd never have chosen her for himself. She was far too old, but he had to go with older, to show Maggie that it wasn't her he wanted any more.

He didn't want to walk with her so he went on ahead and told her to follow him. He glanced back, noticing her funny gait, like she'd had a broken bone up near her thigh and now the leg dragged a little.

He set up the bed. It crossed his mind to ask her for a trick, seeing as she was here and all, but then thought better of it. He wanted a clear head.

"Drop your clothes on the floor."

He needed Maggie to see the items, discarded, so she'd know, so it would be more than obvious.

He had some stout he'd taken home from the pub in a jug and he shared it with her. Then he told her to climb into the bed.

She went to sit astride him, but he pushed her away and said, "No, just wait."

And so they waited, not talking, just sitting.

"Is there anything you'd like to talk about?" she tried.

"No," he said and he got out his tin cigarette box and lit up.

She bent her head and took one from him, puffing on it deeply.

And then, there it was, the knock. It wasn't the usual knock though, a rat-a-tat on the glass. This was frenzied, her knuckles pounding.

"Who's that?" said Blondie.

"No one. Make sure your tits are out, pull the blanket down."

She looked confused but pulled the covers down to reveal her body.

He opened the door slowly, only a bit, poking his head out.

Maggie burst into tears when she saw him.

"*Christy!*" she cried and she pushed forward, so hard it sent him backwards, the door flying open. "*Christy, she's gone. She's gone. She got scalded. I sat up with her all night, but she's gone!*"

She wrapped her arms around his waist and buried her face in his chest.

"Who's gone?" he said into the top of her head.

"Kitty," she said faintly. "My beautiful beautiful Kitty."

He took a step back, shocked with this news she had brought him. And at that moment, Maggie opened her eyes, blinking in the light, taking in the sight of the voluptuous blonde in Christy's bed.

Her eyes trailed from the woman's enormous white breasts, to her red satin dress, to her petticoats and knickers, where they were deposited on the floor.

"*You bastard,*" she whispered.

He held out his hands and went to move forward, but she turned on her heel and ran, out the open door, down the laneway in front of the cottages.

He stood, bare-chested on the doorstep, staring after her into the moonshine.

When he came back inside, he sat at the edge of the bed and planted his forehead into the comfort of the palms of his hands.

"What was that all about?" asked Blondie.

He didn't reply.

"Is that your daughter?" she asked.

"Get out," he said.

"Sorry ... I ..."

The woman got up and started dressing.

Christy lifted his trousers, took three coins from his pocket and threw them down at her feet.

"And have a fucking wash," he said. "You smell like a rotting corpse."

# CHAPTER 28

## *The Nanny*

I was told I was seventeen. I didn't know I was seventeen.

They had the record, they said. I was born there. My mother had delivered me in the sick room, at the back of the workhouse.

I'd never known my age for sure.

I always knew Kitty's age because I counted the years since she was born. She was born in May, on a stinking hot summer's day, my mother moaning in the back room till she appeared all wet and white and creamy.

I washed her gently in soapy water I'd boiled up in a big pan on the hob.

I'd washed my mother too, because the midwife didn't attend. When she came later she said she was off looking after another woman, but I suspected she just didn't want to spend any time attending to Mad Maggie and all that she was.

She said the baby was bonny and healthy and to make sure Ma got the milk into her.

She was aiming that at me. *Make sure your mother gives her the milk.*

But you couldn't rely on my mother. So I asked the midwife if there was other milk I could give her, just in case, and she said I could get formula at the chemist's and, if I couldn't get any of that, to mix bread and goat's milk and warm it up with a bit of sugar in it.

I knew I'd do anything to get the formula milk. The last baby, a boy, had died, after only six weeks. He went all blue, his lips white, and I knew he was on the way out. I cried over that little body.

My mother didn't cry. She said it was probably for the best.

I wanted the girl to live.

And that was how I came to be very good at giving formula to babies. When all the other women and wet nurses were suckling, I was making sure Kitty got the formula, topping her up when Ma wasn't around.

You never knew if Ma would be there or not. And then when she was there, her breath was foul with the drink and I thought if her breath was foul, well, then her milk could be foul. And you could see it in the child, the way she arched her back and spat up after the feeds, so I told Ma that her milk was bad and I'd give her the formula instead.

I got a slap a few times for making comments about my ma like that. But I didn't care. All I cared was that this girl lived.

And she did. I watched fat gather at her wrists and at

her knees and she grew stronger. Before she was even one year old, she was tottering around on her roly, sturdy legs.

It was the formula that saved her.

I often wondered would I have any babies of my own, whether I too would produce them like Ma, but I never did and never did I feel anything stir.

Kitty was a beautiful child. She didn't look like me. I knew I looked stern and sullen.

When Kitty smiled it lit up her face. She had curly hair too, not like my straight hair that hung in clumps around my face.

We didn't know who her daddy was. He could have been any man in this town.

She had her regulars, our ma. I knew them by their voices, by the sight of them behind the raggedy old curtain that hung between the two beds in our room.

They were the ones she drank with, in the piss-poor taverns, the ones that would go home with her and then be gone, probably when they sobered up a bit. None of them wanted anything to do with my ma. Most didn't pay her. Just got her pitchers of beer when she was out, and she was happy with that.

There was nothing for us. That was why I had to do what I had to do.

And with the money I collected, I bought the formula and bread and oats to make stirabout.

I should have been taller. I felt it in my bones, like they wanted to stretch, but the skin wouldn't let it. I felt sunken, living in that broken-down house, waiting to see which men came through, waiting to see if Ma would come home. Waiting to see if Kitty would live another day, because you never knew with young children. And their fevers. And their swollen sticky-out bellies.

And for three years I minded her, mostly on my own.

Until the fight happened, on Christmas Eve.

We were starving and I'd had enough of the freezing cold in the house. I thought I'd go and try and find Ma, and if I couldn't find Ma I'd find someone else to help. A man somewhere.

I brought Kitty because I never left her, not on her own, she'd be too scared. She was such a soft child, clinging to me, tiny, her three years looking like half that on her body.

We walked up the back streets, past the taverns where Ma usually was. I looked in a few, asking people if they'd seen her.

Tiny white snowflakes whipped up around our faces, blown by an easterly wind off the river. It left our noses red, our ears not part of our heads, our fingers, gripped in our shawls, white.

She'd been seen all right. Somebody said she was drinking in the Poet's Rest so we made our way up by the Cellars, up Rosemary Lane, a narrow, soiled street. I took note of who was out, smoking, drinking, looking to paw at me.

If Ma wouldn't give us anything then I could come back here, but I knew if I wanted the good money, I'd have to go down the quays. I'd take them back to our house then but I'd see to them on the settle bench in the kitchen, with Kitty safely locked in the bedroom.

I never let Kitty know what was going on. She would never know what I did to provide for us.

When we got to the top of the alleyway, there was Ma, out on the street, in front of Farley's pub. She was bawling, fighting, and I stood, watching, waiting to see if she'd stop.

There was no point going up to her in this state. She was swinging everywhere, at everyone.

She was a disgrace.

There were people trying to hold her back.

And then she lunged, at a man, tall, with hair so blond it was almost white. He was standing there with his hands up and she dived right at him and he fell down on the ground, and I could see a pool of black blood pissing out of him.

I shielded Kitty's face and ears because Ma was screaming obscenities now, and people were gathering and coming out of the pubs. I stood and watched and when the police came I knew she was done for.

They held her while they attended to the man, roaring at her to shut up and be quiet, and then she was taken away, kicking at them, her legs flying.

Our ma. Drunken, bawling, deranged.

The last time I ever saw her.

I saw the owner come out of Farley's, his wife whispering to him, and he started walking over to us. I didn't want to be caught on the streets loitering. They knew we had no one now.

And so, we left, walking quickly, back down Rosemary Lane. I felt sick having witnessed Ma doing that to the man, knowing that it was the end for her now, for us.

I took Kitty home, not able to face going down to the quays or chatting to the men on the lanes.

There was no food that night. I heated up some water on the pan and we drank that, and I wondered if I could boil up some newspaper or something, something to line our stomachs with.

We managed three days, there, on our own.

On Christmas Day we went and stood outside the priest's house, begging for scraps. The day after, I found a sailor down at the port who took me on board. I brought Kitty in with me, put her on a stool turned face to the wall, and gave her a string and buttons to play with. I wasn't leaving her outside on the quay, or on the deck for another man to find. It had to be done. And that gave us enough to get a few scraps, before we were reported.

It was the priest, I'm sure. Looking at Kitty crying with the hunger on Christmas Day. He was awful sour man, couldn't have just left us to it.

I could have looked after us though. I could have kept doing what I was doing, getting some money, kept us going.

But they were having none of it, the authorities. And so they sent us to the workhouse, because there was no one else to look after us. When we got there and there was a bed each and clothes that had been washed and starched and three meals a day, I thought maybe it was a blessing in disguise.

I didn't have to go off with men any more.

"It's not cold," said Kitty, when she was tucked up in bed, facing me.

In her hand she held a long piece of yellow ribbon. Ma had put in her hair, the day before she was arrested, said it was a Christmas present. Kitty slept with it under her pillow. It was her most precious possession, the only possession she'd ever had. I didn't have the heart to tell her that Ma probably picked it up off the street or yanked it out of another drunken woman's hair or was given it for services rendered.

Kitty treated the ribbon like an animal she'd rescued, washing it in the sink some nights, laying it out beside her in the bed to dry. It began to fray at the ends and I told her if she didn't stop playing with it, it would fray all the way up and she'd have none left then.

That frightened her and she was more careful then,

leaving it under her pillow for a long time, not putting it in her hair as much, until one day I got one of the kitchen hands to singe it a bit on the fire and it sealed it and Kitty was delighted.

"It won't fray now, Maggie, will it?"

"No," I said. "It won't."

And she said, "Thank you, Maggie. Would you like to wear it?"

"Oh no," I said. "It's yours."

"You can have it, just for today," she said.

And she looked so earnest under that mop of curls, that I took it and said all right and I fixed it in my hair and I thought how I'd go to Christy that night and let him see me done up a bit.

I'd felt he'd been pulling away from me, like he wasn't happy with me any more, that I wasn't satisfying him the way I used to.

If I lost Christy, I'd have nothing.

Nothing in the world.

And so Kitty went off, with the other children, running round the yard, and I touched the ribbon in my hair and thought what a sweetheart she was and back with me to the laundry, where the piles of soiled sheets and cottons were waiting for me.

There was protection in that ribbon. I should never have taken it from Kitty, I should have insisted that she kept it and not have put it in my own dark, straight hair.

I think it was blessed, some sort of divine protection my mother had managed to provide for her.

The only thing she had ever given her, in the whole world.

⟡

The tears burst from my eyes as I ran from Christy's

house, the picture of that woman and her big white breasts plastered in my mind. I raced down the lane, past the workhouse wall, past the cottages, past the huts bundled into the side of the road. I ran all the way down the hill till I got to the Dublin road.

The moon was out, hanging over the town, casting silvery riverways along the black water under the bridge. I took a minute to catch my breath, to wipe at my eyes, where the tears were flowing, their own little rivers on my face.

I could not believe Christy would hurt me like that. That he would push away all our whisperings and loving and kissing and take that dirty tramp into his bed.

I knew it though. I knew he'd been straying. I'd been feeling it these past few weeks, in the way he was with me. The look on his face when he answered the door. The way he grimaced when I talked, as if I was boring him, intruding on that little hovel of a house of his.

The way he didn't say anything when I talked about me getting out of the workhouse and bringing Kitty with me.

Kitty.

I spluttered and bent over, panting from the running, choking on the emotion that erupted all the way up from my stomach.

It was me that raised her, that minded her, looked after her.

I told her never to go near that part of the laundry. It was too dangerous with the vats bubbling and the steam and the size of them.

But she forgot. Lost in a game of hide and seek with the others. Up onto the little bridge that went right over those scalding vats and down she fell, her two little legs plunging into the steaming, boiling water.

*A terrible accident,* they said. *So unfortunate.*

The skin peeled off like an onion. It had gone past her waist, all over her bottom. One whole half of her body.

She screamed and she screamed and then she fainted with the fright.

I was in the ironing room and by the time I got to her she was in a bed and the nurse had applied a paste and a gauze to her legs and the bottom of her torso.

But we all knew.

There would be no coming back from that. You didn't get scalded and the skin burnt off your body like that and live.

In and out of consciousness she went. Coming and going. They'd given her something for the pain, but still she'd waken, realise the scald in her legs, cry out and then fall back in a faint onto the bed.

I sat, holding her fingers, the ribbon wrapped round my hand and hers, binding us together.

*I should never have taken it off her.*

"Kit," I whispered softly, "Kitty, you'll be all right, you just got a bad burn. You have to be brave now and let the doctors dress it and you'll be grand. It'll take a while to heal, but you'll be grand."

She'd never be grand.

She was absolutely destroyed.

I sat there, tending to her, wiping a facecloth across her tiny forehead, putting my hand into a glass of water and letting the droplets run off my fingers, into her little rosebud mouth.

She lingered. Coming back to us and going again. Crying and murmuring.

I sat beside her all night, as the shift changed in the infirmary, and in the morning, as the grey light of dawn filtered through the bars on the window at the edge of the ceiling, I realised I'd fallen into a groggy sleep, stretched out across her little arm.

The white starched infirmary covers appeared before my eyes. I sat up and saw Kitty, the trauma of yesterday sweeping back into my addled head.

I ran my hand across her little forehead and her eyelashes flickered.

She opened her eyes and she saw me and there was a little smile before the burning kicked back in and her forehead creased and she started to cry.

"I'm sorry," she said. "I didn't mean it, Maggie. It was an accident."

"I know, pet," I said. "Shush now, don't you worry."

"I thought it would be a good place to hide, but then I slipped."

"*Shhh*," I told her.

"Where's Mama?" she said.

"Ma's not here, I'm here," I soothed.

She hadn't asked after Ma in a long time.

"Mama," she said and started crying again.

"Mama will be here later," I told her, lying, anything to try and ease her suffering. "She'll be here with a big bar of chocolate for you, so she will."

Why was she looking for Ma now, after everything I'd done for her, why was she still looking for Ma?

The doctor came and shook his head. He took me aside and spoke in low, mumbling voice. "You need to be a brave girl now and prepare for the worst."

I already knew it. I wasn't stupid.

I nodded and went back to keeping my vigil at her bed.

And then he appeared, Mr. McGovern, all smirky and slithering, like the snake that he was.

"Little Kate," he said as he stood over the bed, his

face all serious and pouting. "The poor mite. How is she holding up?"

He knew right well how she was holding up.

"It's Kitty," I said.

"A terrible accident," he said. "Don't you worry. You stay here now as long as you need."

I sat in silence, blocking out his presence, annoying him by not responding to him.

"I've asked the nurse to give her everything they can for the pain."

Sure he was a saint indeed.

Would I have let us come here if I'd known what was going to happen to Kitty? Could we have run away, to a different town maybe?

But I knew we would always have ended up in the workhouse. I'd been born here and Ma too.

I gripped Kitty's hand and swore an oath, one that had been swirling round my head, ever since I was old enough to understand what was going on behind that curtain, listening to my ma going at it with another of her filthy bastard johns.

I would be nothing like my mother.

I would make my own life.

I would have everything I ever wanted, as a result of my own hands.

No longer would I sell my body for shillings.

Never would I touch a drop of the drink.

I would get out of this workhouse and I would start a life, one where I had the power, one where I was in control.

She passed at lunchtime, drawing her final tiny breaths, laboured, in pain, floating away when they gave her a full dose of the opium.

And still I didn't cry.

I went back to the dining hall and I ate my pease soup with the others and I thought how I'd go to see Christy that evening, and he'd tell me what to do.

They kept her body in the infirmary, she would be buried in the morning. An unmarked pauper's grave. For an unwanted pauper girl.

⚜

After seeing Christy with that woman, after running down the town and onto the streets, I stayed out the whole night. Walking, wandering. I went down to the quays and I stood there watching the working girls and the men coming and going.

I could smell the taverns, the smoke and the stench of old beer wafting from the open doors, the late houses, the early houses, all the bodies pressed together, damp from the rain, drunk and merry.

I thought about going into the Cellars, sauntering right up to the bar and waiting till someone bought me a whiskey or a port and then having a talk and a laugh and forgetting all about Kitty and Christy and what had happened to me that day.

Forgetting that I was alone in the world now.

But I didn't go into the taverns. I knew the drink and the crush of the bodies and those men looking me up and down, wanting me, would make me feel better for a while. But it would all come back to the same thing. That by doing that, I'd be going just the way Ma did.

I wasn't going to become Ma.

And so I walked. Out under the bridge, past the quays, past the ships moored, gangplanks out, their lamps burning, their goods stacked up high on the shore.

The air was fresh, down by the river, out along Donor's

Green. It grew black, so dark I could hardly see, except for the silvery light that lit the river, a shimmering path flowing straight in front of me.

What would it be like if I jumped in? If I went to the edge, looked and tipped my body over, plopping into the blackness, ripples circling out towards the far bank, edging out to sea?

Would seaweeds and soft tufty water greens stroke my body as I drowned?

Would I meet Kitty down there? Would I see my father, find out who he really was?

I walked to the end of the green and I sat there on the wet ground, listening to the sounds of the park, late at night. Rustling, whoops, a holler in the distance, and somewhere, the sounds of panting.

No. I wouldn't drown. Not tonight.

Somehow, I would get out of that place. I would get away from Christy, from the streets where our mother raised us, where the memory of her echoed in its dirty, broken-plastered walls.

Something changed in me that night. I had poured all my love into Kitty. And now she was gone.

It showed that love did nothing, proved nothing. It was empty.

From now on, I would only worry about me.

From now on, I would be in control.

I would have the power.

The power over anything I wanted in the world.

Even life itself.

What did I care any more? I had nothing left to live for anyway.

# CHAPTER 29

## Mrs McHugh

After the first few weeks, when the shock of losing Mick and waking up each day alone had become a familiar ache, when her routine was settled and her days had a particular, predictable pattern to them, the dreams started coming. At first, the woman was blocked out, shadow-like. She couldn't see her face, but she would appear with her back to her, a silhouette.

The woman appeared in all sorts of manners. In the dream, she would be walking down the road and the woman would step out in front of her. Or she would be attending Mass, kneeling on the pew and the woman would be sitting in front of her, a twitch of her shawl telling it was her – and just as the woman turned to reveal who she was, she'd wake up.

The woman came in the early morning dreams, the ones where she was moving between the deep sleep of night into the sketchy, twilight dawn. Sometimes she would awake with such force and wonder what had woken her. And then as she drifted back, she remembered. It was the woman. The woman in the dark shawl, with the hidden face. The woman who was haunting her dreams.

At first, she thought it might have been her own mother, who often used to be in her dreams when she was caring for her. But her mother had been a heavy-set woman and this woman was thinner and shorter. She knew it wasn't her, just by the aura of her. Her mother was a lovely woman, a gentle, laughing woman.

This woman was something different.

On the nights when the woman didn't appear in her dreams, she awoke feeling fresh, glad that she had managed a night's sleep without being haunted by the strange, eerie presence. On the nights and mornings when she did appear, she awoke feeling tired and strained.

She said some prayers at Mass, praying for better sleep and calmer dreams.

She brought it up with the priest at confession, one Saturday night, before evening Mass.

"Father, there is a woman and she is coming to me in my dreams. I am most disturbed by it all, and it's affecting my sleep."

"Are you having thoughts during the day, of this woman?" asked the priest, from behind the grille.

"No, Father, I don't know who she is. But I feel like I'm being haunted."

The priest was quiet for a moment.

"It's not unusual to have bad dreams when you are grieving. You've suffered a great loss. Disturbed dreams can be most common."

"What if it's the devil, Father?"

"Do you feel that it's the devil?"

"I don't think she has a good spirit, Father."

"Have you noticed anything unusual outside of your dreams?"

"No, Father."

"Anything strange going on in the house?"

"No, Father."

"I don't think it's anything to worry about. I will say a prayer for your disturbed dreams. If anything does happen, you can come to me and I will come and bless the house."

"Thank you, Father."

"And try saying two decades of the rosary in bed, before you go to sleep."

"I will, Father."

After her confession to the priest, she slept soundly for two nights. And then the woman returned.

And this time she saw her face.

⁂

She sorted out Mick's particulars quickly. She got a cheque from the dockers' union and she would get a portion of his pension. It meant she didn't need to work, didn't need to try and sort out anything with Number 43. She could live comfortably.

When she was able, she went through Mick's things. She kept his cap and his pipe but she put all his clothes into a big basket and hawked it down to the second-hand shop, the good one on narrow West Street, so that some other man could make use of them. She got a few shillings for them and with that she bought flowerpots for his grave.

Mick would like that, her being all busy and not maudlin.

Night-time was the worst, sitting there on her own, thinking about him.

During the day she could occupy herself and most evenings there were callers or she'd go down to one of the neighbours. But when she got in, when it was late and he wasn't there to greet her, that was the worst.

She wondered if she'd ever get over the sadness, if the grief that welled up then, choking her, making her head feel like it was swelling and bursting, would always be there. She expected it would. How could it not?

And then there was Betty. She thought they were joking at first when they told her. But their solemn faces and acknowledgment that she was a 'good age' saw the laugh catch in her throat.

Her husband and her closest friend, gone within days of each other.

She never got to talk to Betty about Mick. She never got to talk to her about what happened at Number 43. She had to deal with everything herself, let the thoughts swirl around and around till it made her feel dizzy and she had to start finding ways to stop thinking about things.

She was going to go mad.

A few weeks after Betty's death, a letter arrived on thick paper summoning her to a meeting with Mr. Jennings, Betty's solicitor, on Fair Street. The letter made her feel nervous and she fretted in the days before the appointment. She wondered what on earth he wanted with her? She knew the pub and the rooms above had been left to Jimmy's nephew, a man who lived in England and had not been back to Ireland for years.

On the morning of the appointment she got up early to wash her hair. She put on her Sunday clothes. She felt she should, going to meet a solicitor on Fair Street like that.

She walked slowly down the North Road, turning left onto Fair Street, allowing plenty of time so that she wouldn't appear red-faced or out of breath. Here the railings gleamed in the morning sun, the doors set off by polished brass letterboxes.

The buildings stretched into the sky, doctors, solicitors, dentists, a flurry of people making their way up and down marble and granite steps to their appointments.

Carriages stood, waiting for their passengers to return.

Mr. Jennings' door had a brass knocker with a ferocious-looking lion on it. She knocked and waited to be let in.

A flustered young man opened the door and ushered her in.

He sat her on a leather sofa in the hall and went upstairs, presumably to announce her presence. When he came back down, he ignored her and went into an office off the hall. She could see him going back to his paperwork which was piled high, sighing as he tackled another set of folders.

After an age, a door opened upstairs and a deep voice called out: '*Mrs. McHugh!*'

She felt nervous as she climbed the stairs. If Mick had been alive, he would have come with her. She didn't like having to attend to business on her own.

"Mrs. McHugh," said Mr. Jennings, "please, take a seat."

Mr. Jennings was lanky with dark hair and glasses.

His deep voice was at odds with his appearance. He looked nothing like she thought Betty's solicitor would. What was Betty doing dealing with this chap?

"You are keeping well?" he said, more of a statement than a question.

She placed her bag on her knee and sat forward.

"I'm doing very well, Mr. Jennings."

"I'm sorry to hear about your recent troubles."

"Thank you."

"And I understand Betty Farley was a very good friend of yours?"

"She was, yes."

"Mrs. McHugh, I wish to inform you that you have been included in Mrs. Farley's will. I have the will here and I would like to read the relevant part to you."

She sat up straighter and frowned, listening.

Mr. Jennings started reading, holding the piece of paper close to his nose.

"To my good friend Winnie McHugh, I leave my journals and diaries. She will know what to do with them. I would like her to take anything else she wishes from my rooms. For her troubles, I leave her fifty pounds. She is to spend it on herself, on something nice. Hopefully this will stop her lamenting."

Mr. Jennings looked up at Mrs. McHugh.

"Lamenting?" she said with a laugh. "That woman!"

The solicitor cleared his throat and did not smile. He put the will down.

"I'll arrange for you to meet with Mrs. Farley's nephew next Friday to look over the rooms and collect the journals. Does this suit? I have a bank draft for the fifty pounds here."

"That suits me very well," said Mrs. McHugh.

Fifty pounds. Good old Betty.

❦

The young man behind his pile of papers didn't look up as she walked out onto Fair Street.

What a woman Betty was.

She thought how she was at peace now, lying there beside Jimmy.

She was back where she belonged, beside her great love.

It was wrong to think it, the priest would tell her so, but she knew in her heart that it would be the same for her. That she would go on living, making the best of things, creating a new life, as a widow woman, filling her days as best she could.

But she wouldn't be happy until she met Mick again, until she was in the ground beside him and holding his hand in heaven.

That was the only thing that would bring her true peace. In the end.

❦

All week she had looked forward to going back to Betty's rooms. It would be her final visit, a chance to say goodbye to her after all. It felt strange going up the narrow stairs to the rooms where Betty had lived, knowing she wouldn't be there. The smell was the same, a mix of polish and must.

The room, though, was unrecognisable. Everything had been pulled out, half boxed up, belongings scattered everywhere.

It looked as though Betty had never lived there at all. Gone was the sense of home.

A sandy-haired man was poking in a box, stacking china it looked like. The nephew.

"Hello," he said.

"Hello," she replied and smiled. "So, you're the nephew."

"I am," he said.

"I don't remember her speaking about you much."

"Ah," he said. "Well, it has been a few years."

"It has," she said. "So, what are your plans? You're hardly coming back to Ireland to be a publican?"

"No," he said, shaking his head. "Selling up, I'm afraid. It's a pity. I loved coming here when I was child. And I still love a good pint of Irish stout."

He laughed.

She didn't.

"I have my own business, in Bristol. So, I can't leave, you see."

"I see," she said, looking around the room.

The bed where Betty had lain next to the window was bare now, the mattress uncovered. It looked sad and bereft.

"Did you have anything in mind, that you wanted to take?" he asked, holding out his hand in a sweeping gesture. "I didn't want to pack everything away until you had a look, but I wasn't really sure what you might want."

She scanned the room. She didn't have anything in particular in mind. She walked over to the box of china and took out a blue-and-white porcelain teapot. They had sat over it so many times.

"I think this," she said. "For sentimental reasons."

"The journals are in boxes," he said. "There's quite a few of them."

He pointed to four large boxes on the floor, filled with notebooks and diaries.

"Goodness," said Mrs. McHugh. "Did she really write all of them?"

"Looks like it. If you like I can leave you to have a little look. I'll go and fetch a cup of tea somewhere."

"Oh," said Mrs. McHugh. "That's very good of you."

She was glad that he was leaving her there. She didn't know what to take, if she should even take anything besides the teapot.

When he left, she walked over to the bed and sat on it, looking around the room quietly. She took a breath and listened for a moment, hearing the noise of the street wafting through the window.

Betty loved looking down on all this, watching the world go by. She had a perfect view of the streets below, a perfect of view of Number 43, of the Nanny's bedroom, of the nursery.

She thought of Anna Genevieve, being held by that woman. She thought how the child must have grown by now, her cheeks filling out, her hair growing longer, her smile.

She'd give anything to hold the baby one last time.

She turned her head away. She didn't want to even chance spotting that woman, twitching at the curtains.

"Oh Betty," she said out loud, "you believed me when I told you she was bad news."

She got up and began to potter around the room, looking in the boxes, examining Betty's things.

She found a photo of Betty and put it beside the teapot she was taking.

From a box of clothes she took a heavy fox fur. It was too beautiful to leave and what would a young man like himself do with it only sell it anyway?

When the nephew reappeared, she showed him what she was taking and he smiled and nodded.

"Do you need a hand?"

"I'll need a hand with the boxes," she said.

"I have a lad with a handcart," he said. "He'll run it all home for you."

"Lovely," she said.

"You must have been a great friend to her," he said.

She felt her eyes well up.

"It was she who was a great friend to me."

She turned to go, clutching her basket where she'd placed the teapot and other items she was inheriting.

"One last thing," she said, turning back. "Did you find her pipe? A little white clay thing?"

The nephew scratched his head and walked over to a shelf.

"This?"

"That's the one," she said. "She lived for this pipe. Just like my Mick. May I?"

She held out her palm. He gave it to her and smiled. She put it in her basket and did a final sweep of the room.

"Goodbye, Betty," she said quietly.

As she walked down the stairs, she heard the nephew calling her name.

"*Mrs. McHugh!*"

She looked back to see him hurrying down towards her.

"I almost forgot. When I was moving the locker beside the bed I found this letter. It had fallen under it. It says *Mrs. McHugh* on it, so I didn't open it. That, I presume, is you."

She took the letter he was holding out and looked at it.

"I don't think she knew any other Mrs. McHughs," she said.

She put it in her basket, thanked the nephew for being so kind and went down the stairs to give the directions to the cart boy.

She made sure to keep her head down and not look over at Number 43.

She had a terrible feeling she was being watched.

⤳⤳⤳

She walked slowly home after leaving Betty's rooms, letting all the conversations she'd had with the old woman flow through her mind. Being among her things and now a letter to read when she got home gave her something to look forward to. It had been so long since she had looked forward to anything.

She put the kettle on to boil and took time stirring the tea in her new china teapot. She set the pipe and picture of Betty beside the framed one of Mick on her dresser.

The boxes of journals were stacked in her hall.

She sat in her chair to open the letter from Betty. Behind her lay the fox fur and she reached for it and wrapped it round her neck before she opened the letter carefully.

Betty and a fox fur. Where the hell had she worn that to, the old biddy?

She began to read, intending to let each word settle slowly, reading it as though eating a box of chocolates, savouring this message from the grave.

But the letter was short and written in a scrawling hand. Some of the words were hard to make out. She could tell by the writing that the woman was weak.

When she finished reading, she stood up slowly and walked to the boxes of journals. She took them out, one by one, flicking, searching.

When she found the page with its yellow newspaper clipping, she stared at the police photograph, her hand going to her mouth.

## WOMAN SENTENCED TO LIFE IMPRISONMENT FOR SAILOR MANSLAUGHTER

A whole article on the woman who had been haunting her dreams.

*Winnie, I swear on my life, on Jimmy's life, that nanny is the absolute picture of Mad Maggie. I was wondering all along who she reminded me of and in my stupor of dreams when I was sick, it came to me.*

Mrs. McHugh had never seen Mad Maggie before, only heard about her from Mick, who said she was a scourge.

*Winnie, she's trouble. If that's Mad Maggie's daughter, she's trouble. I don't know if you ever heard the rumours about her and Christy? After he went away it all came out.*

*It's all a bit of coincidence, don't you think, that she came to work with you there across the road? If she knows Christy?*

*Come and see me as soon as you can, and I'll tell you all I know. I'm very tired and it's hard for me to write.*

Black eyes, furrowed brow, her hand reaching out, keening like a banshee.

It was Mad Maggie who was haunting her dreams.

Maybe she *was* a banshee. Maybe someone else was in danger of dying.

She had to let Mr. Thomas know.

But first she needed to take a trip.

# CHAPTER 30

## *The Verdict*

"The jurors for Our Lady the Queen upon their oath present that Margaret Martin late of the parish of Castleknock, with a home at Strawberry Beds, not having the fear of God before her eyes on or about December in the year of Our Lord 1879 feloniously and wilfully did kill and murder one James Andrew Martin, against the peace of Our Lady the Queen her crown and dignity.

Furthermore, the jurors for Our Lady the Queen find that the same Margaret Martin did feloniously and wilfully kill and murder one James Andrew Martin, through the administering of a dose of strychnine on or around the month of December in

*the year of our Lord 1879, against the peace of
Our Lady the Queen her crown and dignity."*

The foreman of the jury stopped reading. The paper
in his hand shook a little. As he'd read, feeling the
words on his tongue, a sense of justice swept through
him and his voice had become louder, confident, a rush
of blood to his head.

He felt quite dizzy.

The parish hall, which held the monthly assizes and
on rare occasions heard the evidence of inquests like
this, was a cold lofty building with floorboards that had
rotted in parts.

To the side of the table and chair assigned to the
coroner, wooden benches had been added to hold the
bottoms of newspaper reporters and press men. The case
had occupied pages across the dailies, dripping detail after
detail about the evil murderess who was on the loose.

A reporter with wide trousers and a green cape that
hung from his shoulders watched the room scrupulously.

He studied the man and woman who had unearthed
the babies' remains, who sat at the front of the hall,
their shoulders hunched, listening intently. So far, he had
not managed to get a break in the story. The *Irish Times*
had got into the house itself and surveyed the garden
where the bodies had been found. They had sat with the
couple and gleaned reams of colour. Their headlines
read **SHOCK AND HORROR AT STRAWBERRY
BEDS** and **'FIND THAT WOMAN AND HAVE HER
HUNG,' SAYS WOMAN OF BABY MURDER
HOUSE.**

The *Irish Daily Independent* had traced a cousin of
James Martin's first wife to Fermanagh who said her
extended family were **"praying day and night for the
eternal souls of the poor twins and their mother"**.

It was the story that kept on giving. Yet, it had given nothing exclusive to him. The *Freeman's Journal* needed a scoop.

A cheer broke the silence of the room, some men leaping to their feet and shaking their fists in the air. The foreman sat down, forcefully, putting his shaking hand in his lap, a blush creeping from his cheeks down past his neck, his verdict delivered.

A fellow juryman leaned over and patted him on the back. "Good man," he said. "Good man."

"*Order!*" shouted the coroner. "*Please, order!*"

The coroner waited until a calm came to the room, murmurings and mutterings tracing over the heads of the dense crowd.

The men and women at the back shuffled and strained to hear what was going on. Most were aggrieved at having to stand so far back – no seats to be got in their own parish hall! From early morning droves of walkers had left neighbouring parishes and made their way to the Strawberry Beds, taking up seats early. Local people who arrived near the time of the court sitting found themselves displaced.

"Thank you, foreman of the jury," said the coroner. "Thank you, jury members. I know many of you were familiar with the deceased and it was difficult to hear some of the more graphic details of the case. Your patience, understanding and time given to this inquest is to be commended."

Poor, affable James Andrew Martin. A very likable fellow by all accounts. Harmless. Not a bad bone in his body. Laced with strychnine, said the analyst, despite the time he'd spent in the ground. It was present in all of the tissues tested.

"The doctors, analysts and chemical experts have,

through their evidence, proved beyond all reasonable doubt that that there was murderous intent in the death of James Martin."

*Beyond reasonable doubt.*

"I would also like to thank the people of Strawberry Beds for their patience and reservation of judgment over these past weeks, while we awaited our analysis. Despite the unwarranted and extended press coverage, the jury have done a fine job in separating fact from fiction."

The coroner looked to the press benches and frowned. Some of the reporters smirked.

"I now issue a warrant for the arrest of Margaret Martin, late of Strawberry Beds for the murder of Mr. James Andrew Martin on or about 17 December 1879. As we are unsure of her whereabouts, I call on all present to do what they can to seek out and find this woman. We will engage with the newspapers and journalists present to spread the word, as well as the authorities and our police forces. Thank you."

"*Hang her!*" shouted a heckler.

"*Murdering bitch!*" shouted another.

The journalists scribbled furiously as the anger continued to erupt.

A rush of men moved towards the man and woman to reach out to them, to seek their opinion on what the coroner had said.

"It is the right decision," said the man. "I hope now that they will find her."

The couple moved off, making their way through the bustle, wishing to be out in the air, away from the packed parish hall. They left through the side door, striding, arms linked, heads down, against a summer wind that had whipped up.

When they were a few paces from the hall, a man

from behind called to them, catching their attention. They stopped and looked around to see a reporter with a long green cape hurrying towards them. He placed a matching fisherman's hat on his head as he caught up.

The man shook his head.

"We have nothing else to say," he said, and he tugged his wife's arm to move on.

"Wait!" said the reporter. "Wait, please!"

He was out of breath.

"I'm from the *Freeman's Journal*. We have an excellent artist who works for us. If I could have a minute of your time, to explain."

He told them that the paper wanted to commission a sketch of the woman. From the man's memory. They were producing a special supplement on the case, outlining every detail of the investigation so far.

"It would help greatly, to find her."

The man looked at the woman. She shrugged her shoulders.

"Very well," said the man. "You can come to the house tomorrow, after work."

"Thank you," he said. "I'm most grateful."

⚜

The children were quiet when they got back to the house, as if they knew that their parents were spent. Today was a pinnacle in the post-discovery calendar.

The woman made a pot of tea, and they sat in the kitchen, not talking, sighing at regular intervals.

They'd only had a few months of contentment in the house. Since the suitcase had been dug from their potato bed, so many boots had crossed the threshold. Neighbours, police, doctors, reporters.

They needed to claim back the house as their own.

The woman sat and thought how, after tomorrow, they would draw a cordon around the house. No one else would get in. They would close every curtain and maybe even barricade the door.

She should have listened to her gut from the start. You could always trust your stomach. You needed to listen to it, to feel it, to take that unease and work out what it meant.

She'd used that feeling since she was a child. When she found herself in situations, in places where she shouldn't have been. In rooms that seemed innocuous enough but when you turned round and everyone was gone and there was only you and that strange boy, the one who was always taking his mickey out and he was blocking the door and you.

The feeling that you needed to escape. Away from the danger, to rescue yourself.

That was the feeling she'd had the whole time since moving into this damned house.

The dissection had been the worst of all – those poor little babies, pulled apart under her roof. She'd heard of post-mortems taking place before, but usually they were in an inn, or a hall, not in a house like hers.

But that was the country way, she learned. It was how things were done. And the scullery would never be the same again.

After the funerals, she had boiled up hot soapy water, mixed it with Jeyes disinfectant and threw in some soapflakes too. She took the hardest scrubbing brush she could find under the sink and scoured the room, the walls, the skirtings, the cupboards. She boiled water over and over, splashing liquid and detergent and fluids all over the scullery and floor.

But still the smell persisted. They didn't put anything back into the room, no food or grains or pots or anything to do with their cooking. She thought they probably needed to raise the floorboards, to take them up and relay new ones, clean ones, ones that didn't have the smell of decay ingrained in them.

He was taking it all in his stride of course, telling her it would all be fine in the end. But she wanted to go. She wanted to go the minute Aidan hit that spade off the case and their whole world was ripped up, laid bare, their happy, peaceful life wiped away.

It was funny though, now that the discovery had been made, now that the babies had been lifted and buried properly, put back alongside their father James, given the send-off befitting of two such souls, that the feeling in her gut had shifted.

No longer did she feel that overwhelming sensation that something was wrong. The strangling feeling in her throat, the sensation that someone was pressing on her neck, the absolute terror she'd been feeling, was gone.

"I want a new floor in the scullery, and I want it whitewashed and scoured again. I can still smell it," she said, breaking the silence over their tea. "I want something done in the garden. Where we found them. A cross maybe and something for Our Lady. I'm not that happy about staying in our bedroom, especially if that poor man met his end there, but I suppose we won't know until they find her, if they get a confession out of her. And I want her found. And caught. Whatever the police have to do, whatever we can do to assist – if this sketch will do it, then so be it. I need to know that we've done everything we can to seek justice for that man and for those poor babies."

"I won't stop until that is done," he said. "And as for

the house, don't you worry, we will do whatever it takes to make it ours again."

"After tomorrow I don't want another set of boots across that door. I don't want this house turning into some sort of horror show. It's already a spectacle."

"I'm sure as time goes on, people will forget," he said.

"We'll see," she said. "All we can do is make the best of it, and try and see to it that that evil, poisonous woman is caught and justice is done. I don't know what else to do for those babies."

She didn't tell him that the only reason she was staying was because she thought the babies' spirits had moved on. If she still had that sense of foreboding, that they were there, watching them, then she wouldn't be staying.

There was no need to discuss it. She knew by her stomach, by her gut. Their souls had moved on now and they, as a family, needed to do so too.

She hoped that woman, wherever she was, wasn't near any more babies or another poor innocent man. They wouldn't last long at her hands if they were, that was for sure.

# CHAPTER 31

*William D. Thomas*

The rocking of the carriage was making him feel ill. He looked across at Margaret and caught her in a smile.

"Feeling queasy?" she asked.

"Yes," he said. "I am rather. I'm not a good traveller."

"Is that why your brother is the seaman and not you?"

"Maybe," he said.

Anna Genevieve slept, her curled-up face tucked beneath blankets in a bassinet that lay on the seat, held fast by Margaret.

They were on their way to Swinford Hall. He wished they were on the return journey now, rocking their way home, instead of towards the estate, set deep in the middle of Meath.

Lush green hills rose in the distance. Birds flew from the ditches as the horses' hooves thundered past.

"You'll like Swinford, I think," he said to Margaret. "It's a very handsome estate."

"Yes," she said. "I can imagine."

"You'll be put up in the nursery no doubt."

"Yes," she said.

She knew that he was apologising already. Letting her know that if he had it his way she would be much nearer, in a guest bedroom, the way it was at home.

They reached Swinford at lunchtime, the carriage turning into a long and winding avenue, shaded by trees, curling into an enormous grey façade with tall gleaming windows.

Their arrival drew Mrs. Winchester to the front door, along with the butler and head housekeeper. They stood to attention as the party dismounted.

"William," said Mrs. Winchester, kissing him on both cheeks. "And little Anna," she said as Margaret lifted the bassinet from the carriage.

She did not address the Nanny at all.

"You are looking well," she said to William. "But you have lost weight. Maybe we can fatten you up a little while you are here."

He smiled, awkwardly.

"My darling," said Mrs. Winchester, leaning into the bassinet when the Nanny placed it on a sofa in the grand drawing room. "Do you know you have made a little bit of history today? You are in your ancestral home, the youngest Winchester. Can you sense it, my little babba, can you feel the importance of it all?"

William clenched his fingers into his hand.

Mrs. Winchester lifted the baby from the bassinet and backed her large behind onto the sofa.

"You can take some tea in the nursery," she said to the Nanny.

Margaret glanced at William and they exchanged a knowing look, before she left the room.

"So how have you been faring?" asked Mrs. Winchester, weighing the child with her hands.

"Things are improving a little," he said. "The business has picked up, Marcus has secured some contracts in France and we'll likely need to take on some new clerks."

"Yes," said Mrs. Winchester, pursing her lips. "I suppose you must return to some form of normality. So tell me ... Anna Genevieve, how has she been? Has she been crying? She's quite light, don't you think?"

"The Nanny says she is doing well."

The child had not stirred.

"Is she sleeping a lot?"

"Yes, I believe so," said Thomas. "She is a very contented baby."

"If she's sleeping a lot then she's not getting the chance to feed. She should be woken."

He looked at Anna Genevieve and didn't say anything. Already, the inquisition, peppered with unsolicited advice had begun. The plain understanding that the Winchesters at Swinford knew best.

"I know the Nanny is doing well, I'm not questioning that – but maybe the doctor could advise. About her weight. About how much she is sleeping."

All those invitations turned down. Why hadn't he found the strength to say no, just one more time?

"Whatever you feel is best," he said, shrugging his shoulders.

He'd found by now that the easiest way to get through any time spent with the Winchesters was simply to be agreeable. There was little point in arguing with Mrs. Winchester. She prided herself in getting her way, in the end.

⁓ᚱᚬᚱ⁓

Swinford Hall was a large mansion house. On the ground floor sat a library, two drawing rooms, a study and a dining hall, that could be used for dancing. He thought about all the rooms surrounding him, about the time he'd spend here over the next three days, roaming, walking the gardens, looking out over the hectares of green estate and orchards.

There was so much space, so much room, so much air, so much land.

And yet he had never felt so stifled. No wonder Anna had run away, fleeing to his townhouse to be with him. No wonder she told him she was the happiest she had ever been, nestled with him in Laurence Street.

Mrs. Winchester had already started her campaign to take Anna Genevieve from him.

If she thought he couldn't see it, well then, she had a very poor opinion of him indeed.

It hardly took a genius to work that one out.

Mr. Winchester had remained in his study. He did not feel up to the welcome party, and while Mrs. Winchester frowned and her mouth pointed downwards in disapproval, she had left him to his brooding in silence.

After a light lunch of soup and sweetmeats they all took a walk in the gardens, pacing out the gravel paths, leading up to the fountain.

"Tomorrow night I've arranged for the Hamiltons to come for dinner – they're bringing their youngest

258

daughter Gwendoline. She is ever so lovely, William, a real lady. Beautiful red curls. You remember the Hamiltons, don't you? I'm sure you met them before. Their father spends a lot time abroad – they were in the sugar industry but they've moved into gas now. Their house is magnificent – they put a lot of work into it, added a gorgeous extension. They have a menagerie to die for."

William nodded several times as Mrs. Winchester spoke.

"I thought it would be nice to have some guests, some company. That'll be nice, won't it, William?"

"Indeed," he said.

The Nanny walked ahead, pushing the perambulator. Anna Genevieve sat upright in the pram, whining a little.

How coincidental that their guests were bringing their daughter. Their single, well-to-do maiden. William sighed and looked ahead at Margaret and the baby. How he wished he was at home in their townhouse, just the three of them. Comfortable. Sipping wine. No one to answer to but themselves.

Reaching the fountain, which was set in the middle of a large gravel square, they took a moment to look at the rushing waters and try and spy one of the large carp that swam there.

Today there was no movement, the fish hovering at the bottom quietly. He pictured a blonde girl at the fountain, remembering his own small stature, running towards her. Anna.

A pang constricted his chest. He wanted to cry.

They turned to make their way back to the house. Ahead a cloud opened and a ray of sunshine poured down, lighting up the great façade.

"Doesn't she look so majestic?" said Mrs. Winchester.

"A very fine house," he said.

"You know my parents fretted about not having a male heir," she said. "They worried that I would not be able to sustain the property, to run it like they did. But they were wrong. They underestimated me."

"They did," he said.

"There's a spirit, I think. A spirit that runs in the blood. Only family could understand."

William didn't respond.

"It's in that baby's blood," she said quietly. She stopped and looked at him. "I know you feel it too. She's the last one left. The last true heir."

He looked after her as she walked on, her skirts sweeping the gravel, the sun ray growing wider, covering the front of the house, sweeping down to the lawn.

⁓⊙⊙⁓

Mr. Winchester appeared at dinnertime, his face the colour of dishwater. He had put on a new collar and shaved. He had made an effort.

William stood up to welcome him when he came into the dining room.

Winchester cleared his throat, walked to the table, sat and looked down at the place mat.

Mrs. Winchester and William sat.

"You are keeping well?" he asked his son-in-law.

"As well as can be expected."

Winchester cleared his throat again. "Good."

The footmen attending dinner began to fuss, folding out napkins, pouring wine, adjusting the utensils.

"Knowing that baby Anna is here under this roof, it simply fills my heart with joy," said Mrs. Winchester.

"Wait till you see her again, dear, she is so bonny. Where would you like to see her after dinner – in the main room?"

Mrs. Winchester looked hopefully at her husband.

After a pause Mr. Winchester nodded his head. "Yes, fine."

Mrs. Winchester smiled.

Over dinner she talked about the gardens and flowers that were in season, about some new shrubbery she would like to import from India, about a play area she intended to build near to the kitchen garden.

"It's beautifully sheltered," she said. "Anna used to play there when she was small. There's an old swing, but our carpenter has some wonderful ideas and said he could build new ones with a wooden slide and maybe even a roundabout. Have you seen those? They're ever so exciting for small children?"

William nodded, his head bowed.

He looked up when he realised she was waiting for an answer.

"I think the baby is a bit small for swings and roundabouts?"

"It's good to plan ahead," she said sweetly.

"Indeed."

She talked again of the Hamiltons, telling William all about the family's background and dropping Gwendoline's name whenever she could.

"Oh, I can't wait for you to meet her, William, she really is a darling."

The thing he'd loved about Anna was that she had no interest in attending social events and was not a socialite like her mother. She didn't have to meet new people, make small talk and organise great big dinners to feel worthy, to feel that she was doing something with her life.

They retired to the main drawing room, a room that had always been in use up till recent times. Now that Mr. Winchester had taken to his moods, Mrs. Winchester usually went to her lady's drawing room in the evenings, leaving her husband to his study or to his billiards room or to the library where she knew he kept a special stash of sherry.

Red wallpaper with velvet brush covered the walls of the main room. Family portraits hung large and imposing, separated by smaller oil paintings. Mrs. Winchester had displayed her large porcelain and silverware collections in various walnut cabinets.

After a round of drinks, the door opened quietly and the Nanny walked in, carrying Anna Genevieve who was now awake, her small, black eyes blinking in the warm glow of the drawing room.

Mr. Winchester sat in the armchair beside the fire, one knee crossed over the other. He stared into the flames, a blank expression on his face.

"Oh look!" said Mrs. Winchester. "She's here."

She sat back on the sofa and threw her arms out. "Give her to me."

The Nanny bent down and gave her the child.

"Well, will you look! You are just the picture of your mother. The picture!"

William stayed with his back to the fire, smiling at the sight of his daughter. He looked across at Margaret who smiled back.

"Has she been faring all right in her new surroundings?" he said.

"Yes," she answered. "The nursery is warm and she has fed well today."

"Wonderful," said Mrs. Winchester. "That'll be all for now. You can take some supper to the nursery or if you'd prefer to eat with the staff, they usually dine about now."

Margaret looked at William and bowed her head. He felt guilty. If only his mother-in-law would engage in some conversation, instead of talking down to her, they would see her charms for themselves.

He longed to go after her when she left. To tell her not to mind Mrs. Winchester, that soon they would be home and back to their own comfortable set-up at Number 43.

Instead he asked for another glass of port.

"It's so lovely to see her awake. And I see she's been dressed in the new clothes I got her. How quaint!" said Mrs. Winchester.

Mr. Winchester had turned his head from the fire and was looking in their direction a little curiously.

"Come and see the child," she ordered.

With effort Mr. Winchester left his chair and came and stood over his wife and granddaughter.

"Yes," he said. "Very good. Very lovely."

"Oh, do sit down and have a go. She really is the most beautiful creature."

Doing as he was ordered, Mr. Winchester sat on the low sofa and was forced to hold out his arms as his wife thrust the baby towards him.

"Take a good hold of her there now and look at her."

Mr. Winchester sat ramrod straight. The baby began to whimper.

"Well, that's such a sight – what a little beauty!" said Mrs. Winchester, letting her husband get used to the feel of the baby.

"Do you see the curve of her brows, just there?" she said, after minutes of silence. "That's Anna. That is exactly how Anna looked when she was a baby."

Mr. Winchester shuffled a little, trying to make the baby more comfortable. He cleared his throat. "Yes," he said. "She does look like Anna."

They were quiet again, until the crackle of a log splitting in the fire made the baby jump.

To the absolute horror of everyone in the room Mr. Winchester suddenly let out a howl, followed by an enormous sob. He began to cry, loudly, his shoulders shaking, the baby shaking with the movement too.

Startled, she too began to wail, a high-pitched piercing cry.

William moved toward the baby, to take her, to comfort her.

"No," said Mrs. Winchester and she waved him away while putting a hand on her husband's racking back.

Tears rolled down Winchester's cheeks, past his chin, plopping onto the baby's chemise.

"My poor Anna," he said, his voice hoarse.

Mrs. Winchester patted his back and looked softly at William.

"There, there," she said. "There, there."

The baby stopped crying as if sensing a greater distress than hers and continued to look upwards through her black eyes at her weeping grandfather.

After a while, the sobs stopped and William asked if he should take the baby.

"I'm happy to hold her," said Winchester.

Drinks were poured, more port for William, glasses of sweet sherry for Mrs. Winchester.

Anna Genevieve's grandfather drank no more.

He clutched the child until the Nanny returned and removed her from his arms to put her to bed.

When she was gone, Mr. Winchester left his chair silently and walked from the room. When the door closed behind him, William and Mrs. Winchester looked at each other.

"I've never seen him like this," said William.

"Grief does strange things to people."

"He loved her so."

"He did."

"We all did," said William.

# CHAPTER 32

## *Mrs. McHugh*

As the train raced along the tracks, the green fields speeding by, she realised it was a trip she should have made more often. It wasn't too taxing of a journey really. The longest part was when she got off the train at the small one platform station at Kells and had to make her way to Susan's farm, a distance of eleven miles.

Catherine, her niece, was waiting when she stepped out into the warm breeze in the small station yard, her hands on the reins of the dappled pony they used for getting about. The sky clouded over as they pulled out of the station and made their way down the winding country roads towards the farm.

She was glad Catherine had come. She enjoyed her

niece's company and they passed the time observing the weather and catching up on the various marital, birth and death situations of their neighbours.

Catherine said they were glad that she was coming to visit.

"Mam's been worried about you. It'll be a nice break for you on the farm for a while."

"Arrah, no need to be worrying about me," said Mrs. McHugh, shrugging off the sentiment.

"How long are you staying, Auntie Winnie?"

"Oh, just tonight," she said.

Catherine looked surprised.

"Ah, you'll have to stay longer than that! Sure you've come this far."

"There's something I need to attend to at home."

"Right you be," said Catherine. She hoped her mother would be able to persuade her aunt otherwise.

Susan welcomed her to the farm, coming out of the farmhouse and giving her a quick embrace.

"Winnie, I knew you'd come to see us eventually."

They went inside for tea and brack, the fire smoky with turf. A large open grate centred the kitchen, knickknacks, bric-a-brac and candles littered the mantlepiece above it. Mrs McHugh smelled the distinct farm smell that had seeped into every piece of cloth and wood in the place. Manure, fresh and old, unpleasant and comforting.

Susan was full of chat. It was nice to be in the cosy kitchen, with the comings and goings of Catherine's children, getting the tea ready for the men coming in later.

As they washed baking tins and scone trays, Susan said in a low voice so that no one could hear, "How are you faring, pet? Are you doing all right? You're looking well, I must say. It can't be easy on you. I was delighted to hear you were coming down, break up the week for you."

"I'm grand. I'm getting used to things. It's lonely now, I have to say that. But I'm keeping myself busy. And the neighbours are good, I usually go down to them on Saturdays and Sundays."

"Ah, that's good," said Susan.

"Actually," said Mrs. McHugh, "when you get a chance, Susan, I need to talk to you about something. It's why I've come down."

"Is everything all right?"

Mrs. McHugh nodded.

Susan wiped large suds off a small greasy bowl.

"Is it about Christy?" she whispered, looking a little guilty now.

"Can we go for a walk after tea?" said Mrs. McHugh.

"Aye," said Susan. "Aye, no bother at all."

⁓◈⁓

The air was warm, but the sky was now black with clouds. They gathered in clumps, threatening rain and thunder too. The cows were out to pasture, lying down in anticipation of the rain, chomping their way through long thick grass, their jaws moving at an angle.

They walked up the back fields, climbing an incline till they got to a vantage point, offering a sweeping view of the Boyne Valley. Mint, yellow and frog-green fields rolled in every direction, cut by dark, thorny hedges.

It was good to be out in the country air, where the atmosphere felt different, the breeze awash with something nourishing, wholesome.

Mrs. McHugh drew the air into her lungs, taking a long breath in and letting it out slowly.

"Is he out?" she said, staring at the view, looking at the cows moving like miniatures now.

"Christy?" said Susan. She felt her sister tense a little. "He is, he's out. He's living in Dublin."

"So you're in contact then."

"We are."

"How long have you been in contact?"

"Winnie …" said her sister, looking across at her now. "What is this all about?"

"What do you know about a girl called Margaret, Mad Maggie's daughter?"

"Who?" said Susan.

"You heard me."

"Mad Maggie's daughter?"

"Do you know who I'm talking about?"

Susan looked off into the distance and then back to her sister.

"There was a girl, years ago, before he went inside. I know he'd been seeing her. She'd been in the workhouse. Is that her?"

"A young girl?"

"She was young at the time. He mentioned her to me the odd time but told me nothing much."

"What happened to her?"

"I don't know. The court case happened then and that was it really. But he did mention the name Maggie a few times in his letters. A friend of his."

"It's the Nanny."

"What?"

"The Nanny."

"What nanny?"

"The whorin' nanny at Number 43, the one who got

270

me sacked, before Mick died!"

"How – how could that be?"

"She'd be the right age. And I've seen a picture of Mad Maggie, her mother. They're identical."

"What has this got to do with Christy?"

"What sort of contact were you in with him?"

"Just the odd letter. Winnie, he's my brother."

"He's my brother too."

"I know, but ... I couldn't leave him to rot in there."

"I could."

"I know you could. But ..."

"But what?"

"It was a mistake, Winnie. He made a mistake."

"It wasn't a mistake, Susan. It was a plan. He planned to do that, in my house."

"I know that but ... ten years, Winnie. His life over."

"So, this is my fault then. I'm still to blame."

"I just don't see why you're so angry with me for writing to him. It was the Christian thing to do."

"Christian!" spat Winnie.

Her cheeks had flushed now with anger. Over the years, Christy's incarceration had punctured their get-togethers, rearing the same accusations, the same blame, against her. Only Mick had backed her in her decision to stand against her brother.

"Did you tell him about Number 43?"

Susan folded her arms. "What do you mean?"

"Did you tell him about what was going on, that we were looking for a nanny?"

"I might have done."

"Well, that's it then. He told that woman about the position and, lo and behold, she arrived. This comes back to you, Susan. This is on you."

"How is it on me?"

"They set me up for theft. I could have been jailed, for God's sake!"

Mrs. McHugh set off walking, taking great big strides through the grass. Her sister followed, urging her to wait, but she swung her arms, going faster. When she got to a gate, she didn't open it, instead clambering over it with effort.

"Will you be careful!" cried Susan.

When they got near the house Mrs. McHugh turned and looked at her sister.

"I'll stay tonight but I'm going first thing in the morning. I'm going to go and talk to Mr. Thomas, tell him what I know, that this woman has connections to my criminal brother and the theft case is all some big – some big act of revenge to get back at me."

"Winnie, this is ridiculous."

"Is it? I don't know, Susan. I'm not the one in touch with our molesting brother. You'd be more aware of what he's capable of than I would."

Back at the farmhouse, she swung open the front door into the kitchen. Susan's husband, Catherine and her children all looked up, smiling, ready to welcome her for an evening of conversation around the fire.

"I've come down with an awful headache," she said. "I'm sorry but I'm going to have to go so sleep, it's the only thing that cures it."

She went to bed, to the small back room they'd made up for her, the sheets a bit damp and smelling of turf.

After a while, Susan came in with a hot-water bottle wrapped in a pillowcase.

"Would you like a cup of tea?" she asked.

"No, thank you, Susan," she said. "I'm sorry, I'm just not up to conversation tonight."

"That's all right."

Both women were quiet for a minute.

Susan broke the silence.

"I'm sorry, Winnie. I never meant to do anything to upset you."

"I know that. But Christy's dangerous. He has you all wrapped around his little finger – you just can't see it. I needed to know. I needed to confirm there was a connection between the Nanny and him. I have that now."

Susan pursed her mouth. "I'm sorry for any part I've had to play in all of this."

"Arrah, it's done now."

"Goodnight, Winnie."

The room was still lit by summer light. She tossed and turned, going over all the slights the Nanny had inflicted, the constant smirk on her face, the horrible knowledge that the woman knew all about her all along.

That night her dreams were muddled, cursed, Christy and the Nanny's grimacing faces all coming at her, up close and far away. Anna Genevieve appeared too, before Mad Maggie scooped her up and took her off, sending a wave of panic through her, jolting her from her wretched sleep. The hot-water bottle was cold at her feet.

⋙⋘

In the morning, she was tired, and she wanted to get home, back to her familiar surroundings, back to Drogheda.

"What are you going to do?" asked Susan.

"Well, I'll have to go and speak to Mr. Thomas, won't I?"

"You could call to him at his office," said Susan helpfully. "If you didn't want to go to the house like."

"That's not a bad idea," said Mrs. McHugh. "Aye, maybe that's what I'll do. He's very fond of that woman though. It'll be hard to make him see what I see. To explain, about Christy."

"Would you take the job back, if he offered it?"

"I don't know. Not with her there, certainly."

"Good luck, Winnie."

"Thank you, Susan. I'll need it."

# CHAPTER 33

## *Christy*

It wasn't his fault that the girls liked him. That's the way they made it out in court, that it was his fault. But how could it be his fault? It wasn't as though he'd chased them? It was them who came to him, wanting, looking for something, money, cigarettes.

Young ones, on the streets. Paws out. When you got talking to them and got them smiling, well, what was the harm in that? Making them feel better, he was. Unless it was their first time of course. That usually shocked them a bit.

And better him to be their first than some old pervert. You always remembered your first. He was kind to them, gentle, they appreciated that, so they did. Told him that, cuddling up to him, hugging him, asking him for a smoke, asking could he get them a jug of beer.

He could get them anything. They loved that about him.

Maggie had been a bit older than he liked. There was a nice age, before that, when they were old enough to know what was going on, but young enough still to be innocent. That was his favourite age. Maggie was well experienced when he met her. Still, she was regular, always around and he wasn't going to say no.

He was sorry the way it happened though, with the accident and her sister and that woman in his bed.

That was shocking bad timing so it was.

He felt real sorry about that.

He'd got out the whiskey after the whore had left, drinking it till the bottle was dry, then headed out to the tavern at the top of the hill for more. When he awoke the next day, his tongue sandpapered, his head bouncing, he thought he'd need to stay away from her for a while.

She'd be in the horrors now with her sister gone.

He asked to change his shift at the workhouse and they took him off the runs there and put him onto the coal yard, which was a shocking dirty job, but he needed the space from Maggie.

It was hard to explain, even to himself. He just wanted to forget about her. To let her off, have her find her own way, to get away from the drag of her, on at him about marrying and rescuing her from that place.

In the evening times, when he passed by the back wall of the workhouse, he often looked at the stones, to see if they had moved, to see if they might even be moving right there and then before his eyes, Maggie and her dark hair popping out to say hello.

But they never did. And she never came near him again.

In time, he missed her.

One day he was put back onto the workhouse run, to cover a shift and as he helped roll the drums in their carts into the back hall of the laundry, he asked one of the girls if Maggie was there.

"She's gone."

"Gone?"

"She got a placement. In Wicklow. Ah, she's gone a while now."

He couldn't believe it. He shouldn't have waited so long to try and see her.

Maggie gone.

"Do you know where?" he asked the girl.

"No clue," she said and shrugged her shoulders.

There was nothing he could do, no way to reach out to her. He couldn't march into the industrial office and demand an address.

So, he tried to forget about her.

Maggie and all her sorrows. Mad, just like her mother. He told himself he was better off without her.

But she wouldn't get out of his head.

⁂

It was a mistake, a stupid mistake. He should never have let it happen. They never needed to go into the house at all. They could have gone to that laneway or stayed in the cart even. Going into the house was a mistake.

He'd been with the young one a few times before. A skinny lass, quiet enough, a bit grubby, like they all were. She'd been brought up in the orphanage at Bolton Square, parents long dead from disease or poverty, something anyway that sent her there when she was only a tot.

And like the rest of them, all she wanted was a bit of affection, a bit of love. She was a soft thing. But, Jesus, she was sweet.

He was coming back from Collon, a haul of stones in the back of the cart. It was a favour for a fella he drank with – he shouldn't even have been out that way, but he'd get a few drinks on account of it that night.

There she was, walking up ahead, at the top of the North Road, her spindly legs sticking out of the skirt.

That was the thing about the young girls. They were still in the short dresses.

Her blonde hair flashed in the sun. He let the horse pull right up beside her. It startled her when it stopped.

When she saw it was him, she smiled.

"Hello," she said.

"Hello to you," he replied. "What brings you all the way out here then?"

"Never you mind," she said.

He laughed. "Would you like a lift?"

He helped her up to sit beside him, at the front of the cart.

She was thin, her little wrists pure bone. She rested her palms on her knees, the sinews clear in her hands.

"Are you hungry?" he said.

She looked at him, her eyes wide.

She was always hungry.

He could bring her back to his cottage the far side of town – he'd brought her there before. But there was nothing to eat there. He could take her to a café down the town or ...

He saw the house up ahead near the top of the North Road.

"I know just the place," he said.

He pulled the cart into the laneway behind the row of cottages, tying up the mare, patting her on the nose.

He took the girl by the hand and led her past the whitewashed back walls of the houses.

"Where are we going?" she asked in her sweet voice.

"Somewhere that's warm and has the best bread and jam you'll ever have in your life."

He got to the cottage, the house he was raised in, the house where every brick was as familiar as the back of his hand and opened the back gate. He took the key from under a saucer on the window ledge, where it had been kept ever since he was a boy.

"Oh, this is lovely," said the girl, looking around at the kitchen that smelled of baking. The range was still stoked.

"This is where I was born," he told her. "My sister lives here now. With her husband."

"Oh," she said. "It's very nice. It's much nicer than yours!"

He smiled at her insult, which had no malice behind it. And it wasn't untrue.

He made her bread and jam and she ate it hungrily, licking her fingers when she was finished.

"Would you like some more?"

She nodded.

"How about tea?"

He put the kettle on to boil on the stove and looked around the house.

Saint Winnie and her martyring ways.

She'd done it on purpose, setting herself up in the house to look after their ailing mother. She knew what she was doing, pushing everyone out so that she was the only one caring for her.

The house should have been his. All the others were off seeing the world, making their riches, and Susan over there in Kells with her rich farmer husband.

Winnie got the house. And what did he get?

They drank their tea at the table, cream floating from the fresh milk.

"This is lovely," she said. "Where is everyone?"

"My sisters is a housekeeper, her husband is down the docks. Waste really, isn't it, no one here all day?"

"Yes," she said. "It's so cosy. I'd love to live here."

"So would I, pet."

When they were finished their tea, he took her into the bedroom, the spare one, his old room and told her what to do. She obliged, her belly full. Christy made her feel older, like a woman almost, special.

It was over quickly, the thrill of being in his sister's house, in his old bedroom, somewhere he shouldn't have been with this young saucy thing, overwhelming him. She giggled as he groaned and he slapped her on the bare arse.

"Will we have another cup of tea?" she asked.

"Ah, we'd better be going," he said, thinking of the mare tied up outside.

In the kitchen he lifted his jacket from where he'd draped it across the hard-backed kitchen chair and swung it across his shoulders. She touched his arm, helping him into his sleeves and he leaned down to kiss her.

He felt himself readying again.

"C'mere, you," he said, swinging his bottom down into the chair, taking her straddling onto his lap. "You do something to me, you know that?"

She laughed.

They joined together again, this time more slowly and

he held her tight, his face contorted, concentrating on nothing but the soft, wet feel of her.

Neither of them heard the front door open or the pad of the leather boots on the hall floor. Neither of them flinched when the door of the kitchen opened and the woman stood, her mouth agape at the sight that greeted her in her own home.

"*Christy!*" she shouted, startling them both.

The girl leapt off him to stand, shocked, her arms up as if expecting blows.

"*Get out!*" Winnie screamed. "*Get out!*"

They fled, out the back door, him pulling up his trousers as he ran, the girl in front of him as Winnie stood and watched.

He leapt into the cart and pulled her up behind him.

"Will you get in trouble now, Christy?" she said.

"Ah, she'll be all right," he said. "Hysterical when she wants to be. I'll just give her a wide berth for a week or so."

But he'd underestimated his sister. He didn't realise the depths Winnie McHugh was about to go to, in search of justice.

He let the girl off near Bolton Square and dropped the stones off at his pal's house, throwing them one by one quickly into the yard. He wanted out of there, he wanted home, he wanted a drink.

When he'd dropped off the cart and walked up the hill to his cottage, going in to get some money so that he could go back out again, he found an envelope, shoved under the door.

He opened it, standing in the doorway, not even closing the door behind him.

It was from Maggie. She was in Wicklow. She wanted to see how he was, send him her address.

A letter. From Maggie!

As he reread her words, which were written in a poor scrawl, her letters practised and new-looking, he heard footsteps behind him.

He turned, to find two policemen standing on his doorstep, silhouetted in the early evening sun.

"Mr. McCoy?" said the taller one, his face solemn. "We've had a report about an incident between you and a young girl."

His hand was on his baton.

"We have a few questions for you."

# CHAPTER 34

*The Nanny*

After Kitty died, I started taking lessons in reading, writing and arithmetic. I'd never got a chance to go to school regular and I knew if I wanted to be able to move up in the world, I needed to be able to read and look at things and understand.

I sat with the other younger students, not caring that I was the tallest and oldest in the class, ignoring their stifled giggles when the tutor asked me a question. I ignored the parts on the Catechism and religion and God, they were of no use to me. What I needed was knowledge that would help me get employment, that would help me to read hard books, that would allow me to hold conversations like a lady.

That's what I saw myself as. That's what I wanted to be.

A lady.

Kitty's bed stayed empty beside me and after the first few nights I went to the dorm matron and asked to be moved, away from the memory of her, of her little face, waking up to mine each morning.

She obliged.

I went to the far end of the dorm and watched as my bed was filled by an older woman, who was a drinker, just like Ma, and Kitty's bed by a girl younger than me, her face so gaunt she looked as if she'd already seen hell and come back to visit us all.

Kitty's absence followed me like a ghost. Most of the time I pretended that she'd never even existed, scrubbing at the washboard feverishly in the laundry, the skin tearing off my knuckles till the blood starting soaking into the water and the white sheets and I got a clatter for that and was put on ironing instead.

I used the laundry as a distraction. The lessons as a feast for my mind. I didn't know when I'd be leaving here or how, but I knew it would be soon.

I could feel it.

In the end, it was himself who called me up, old Snake Eyes McGovern, his pupils squinting at me as I came in the door.

He didn't tell me to take a seat. That would be too respectful for me. Instead he let me stand there, my hands behind my back, gawping at him.

"Our records show you are seventeen, Margaret," he said, flicking over a piece of paper on his desk.

Seventeen. So that was my age.

"Some time ago you expressed interest in leaving, finding a placement."

My ears pricked. This was it. This was the door out.

"I know you are taking lessons. And you have been working hard. You have improved, shall we say?"

He was falling over himself with the compliments altogether. He paused, waiting for me to react, as if I should smile or something at him, but I kept my mouth straight and stared.

"I've been contacted by a woman here in Drogheda, who is looking for a good servant girl for a house in Wicklow. It's her sister's house and they haven't had much luck in finding the staff they need. She's keen to give someone a chance."

I watched his eyes squint, just a little more.

"I thought of you."

Wicklow. My escape would be Wicklow.

"If you are agreeable you can leave tomorrow. The train will take you most of the way there and they will meet you at the station. I will telegram ahead."

I nodded.

I wanted to smile, the delicious sense of freedom, of something new, of something wonderful was seeping through me. But I didn't want to grant McGovern any of this pleasure.

"There's something else," he said. "We've a had a letter from Grangegorman. Your mother hung herself by her bedsheets a fortnight ago. I'm sorry. I think she took the news of your sister's death very badly."

Ma. Dead. Just like Kitty.

Not a soul in the world left related to me.

I continued to stare at him. I didn't even flinch.

"I think with this news and what happened over the past few weeks, it is fair that you get a chance, that you get some sort of fresh start."

He felt guilty about Kitty.

"I wish you well, Margaret. I hope we won't see you back here."

"You won't," I said, the only words I allowed him.

I made my way back to the laundry where I finished my work. Over tea, I whispered to the girls around me that I was going, that tomorrow I'd be gone.

They were excited for me, told me they were jealous. Later one of the girls plaited my hair.

The next morning, I was given a canvas bag, a freshly laundered dress, new underwear and a set of second-hand boots.

I slipped out the back just before I was due to go out the front door, to the train station on my own. I walked quickly to where Kitty lay, nothing on her grave only a big mound of fresh earth, someone else new in it.

"Goodbye, Kitty," I said, clutching her ribbon in my hand. "I will make something of myself, you wait and see."

I wanted to give her back the ribbon, I wanted to put it on her grave, to say sorry, to say goodbye. Instead I tied it round my hair and let a tear drop down my face until I sniffed and shrugged and made myself forget.

I wanted it for protection.

As I walked out the front gate, my canvas bag in my hand, my new shoes clobbing, my thoughts moved from Kitty to Christy.

He wouldn't know where I was gone. He wouldn't be able to find me.

I couldn't help wanting him to want me.

Maybe I'd write to him when I got there.

Tell him I forgave him and it was all right if he wanted to write me back.

I had no one else in the godly world, no one at all, that was mine. And I missed him.

❧

The house in Wicklow was the loveliest house I'd ever seen. There were no holes in the walls or plaster showing or a stink coming from rotten drains and pots thrown outside.

There were curtains and paintings and dark wood panels on the walls, oil paintings everywhere, luxuries I'd never even imagined.

The light streamed in through tall windows and I marvelled at the furnished rooms, wallpapered, cushions on the sofas, deep-set rugs on the floors. Who knew people lived like this?

The work was hard enough. We were expected to keep everything dust-free and clean and there were so many knickknacks to be gone over with the cloth, all the silver to be polished, brass to be gleamed.

But it wasn't as hard as the laundry. And the food here was full of salt and butter and other tastes that had never been in my mouth before.

It took me a while to settle in, because I didn't know so many things and the housekeeper called me a 'stupid girl' when I'd first arrived. But I wasn't stupid. I just wasn't learned in living in a lovely house like this.

After about a year, I knew I had settled well. I started to read the books that were left in the common room we shared, going over the big words, looking them up in the dictionary. I read the newspaper every evening, looking at the pictures and stories from all around the world.

After two years, I'd earned their trust completely. Sometimes when the Nanny was busy, her hands full, or she needed to go to the village or into the town, I was the only one who could be spared to look in on the children.

I'd sit with them, playing their games, listening to their prattle and their high-pitched voices and grand accents. They said their words as if there was a big 'o' in the middle. At first, I loved looking after them, getting out of cleaning duties for a few hours, watching how they played with their toys and drew pictures and embroidered little cushions.

Over time though, I began to take against them. They were an obnoxious lot, fighting, crying and whinging over the slightest of things. If Kitty had only half of what they had …

The resentment grew inside me like a rot.

One day, when I was asked to bring their tea tray up to the nursery, I decided to play a trick for fun and heaped two big teaspoons of salt into their puddings. I knew they'd gag and complain about the cook and be all put out for the evening. That made me laugh.

I couldn't stand their whinging and moaning, grumbling over everything that wasn't even a problem at all.

When the nanny took ill, I was assigned to the nursery until they got a temporary replacement. I smiled and joked and planted a great big grin on my face.

But I was smiling at the thought of a plan. An idea that had nestled in my head and wouldn't go away.

I was going to teach them. I was going to show them that they needed to appreciate what they had.

I'd got the idea from the newspaper, a case in England where a wife was up in court for poisoning her husband.

She did it to get back at him for beating her and, I thought, I could do that to those kids, just a bit to warn them, to say you don't know how bloody lucky you are.

When they were good, things would be good. When they weren't, they would suffer the consequences.

It became a bit of a game. I snuck the poison from the back hall, sprinkling a tiny dusting of the white rat powder into soups, or folding it into their sandwiches.

I learned there were other solutions and syrups that could help control the nursery. When the baby was tired and cried too much, I'd add a good dose of soothing syrup to her bottle, just like our ma used to do to us.

When the girl, with her airs and graces and love of sticking her nose in the air was argumentative and grating, I'd drop the soothing syrup into the milky porridge she had for supper. I alternated between soothing syrup and poison for the boy. He was an awful, annoying wheedling chap.

I learned how to administer the doses in just the right amounts – I needed to keep them just sick or sleepy enough not to arouse suspicions. I didn't want doctors called and I didn't want them to associate any of the illnesses with me.

I got a thrill from it, watching how I could control them. How I had the power. How I could teach those children to behave, to be a bit more grateful, to realise there were so many children, so many little girls and boys locked up in workhouses and rundown shells of houses, freezing, hungry, forced to the street to look for scraps and they didn't lament nowhere near as much as them.

I didn't mean to do away with that baby.

It was an accident. I was measuring a bit of rat powder out onto a spoon and the box tipped and more went in than I wanted. I heard footsteps on the stairs and I needed to pick up the tea tray, get out of there, not be caught interfering with the baby.

It was a shock when the nanny found her in the morning, cold in her cot.

The mistress was distressed, everyone crying.

But after, when it was all dealt with, when nursery life returned to normal, I realised I was soaring inside.

Only I knew the real truth of what happened.

Only I had the power, the control over their little precious lives.

Sure it was like I was God himself, deciding what punishments needed to be handed out.

I had come up in the world, just like I swore I would.

# CHAPTER 35

## *The Witness*

A dog barked, vicious. It looked like a mastiff. He put his hand down, out and flat and let the dog smell it. It was cautious, its nose quivering, sniffing, but not touching his fingers. It stopped barking and backed up as he opened the wooden gate.

The small yard was swept and clean. Lavvy pots were stacked outside to be washed. A cart was stacked with turf ready to be unloaded.

He patted the dog on its head, and it wagged its tail slightly.

He always had a liking for dogs. Loyal creatures. Maybe he'd get one for himself.

If he didn't find a wife.

He rapped on the back door and watched a woman appear, behind the glass panes.

"I'm looking for Eliza," he said. "Eliza Butterly?"

"Yes, that is I," she said, eyeing him curiously, taking in his long green cape and wide hat.

"I'm here about your letter," he said. "You wrote to the *Freeman's Journal*. About a woman you worked with?"

Blushing, the woman closed the door behind her gently and stepped out.

"*What are you doing here?*" she said, her voice a hiss.

"The editor was extremely interested," he said. "I would like to interview you, to find out more. Do you think your employers might grant an interview too?"

The woman looked mortified.

"I'll be sacked. Please, you must leave. I wrote on the letter that I wanted my name withheld."

"If I could just ask you some questions. Your letter could be of vital importance. This is a very serious matter."

The woman looked behind her.

"Can you go out beyond the gate?" she said. "I'll meet you there in a minute." She ducked back inside and he walked slowly from the servant's entrance and across the yard. He carried a camera, a wooden tripod and a large leather bag.

He looked back at the house, noting its bay windows to the front. It was one of the bigger houses on the road and looked respectable, affluent.

Was this where the woman had started her killing spree?

Eliza reappeared, wearing her cloak and bonnet. She set off walking as soon as she got to the gate, and he followed her, the dog bounding beside them.

"You shouldn't have come," she said, agitated. "You could have written first and I would have met you."

"I'm sorry," he said. "We thought it better if I followed up immediately. This really is too important a case. We are carrying out our own investigations and we will be handing all information over to the authorities."

He didn't tell her that the most pressing issue was *The Freeman's Journal* eight-page supplement, which had promised details, exclusives and titillating coverage for those interested in the case. The print run had already been doubled.

"Could you tell me about the woman?"

The maid didn't answer and kept walking.

"I don't want this brought on me," she said, suddenly stopping and looking at the reporter direct. "I can give you information, but I wish to remain anonymous."

"Let's get the information and we'll see what we'll do next," he said.

Dissatisfied, she walked on, folding her arms. They reached a wooden bench, set back from the road. She sat on it and he joined her.

"I will tell you what I know," she said. "But I am only doing it because I believe that she has done wrong and I want to stop her. If it's true what she did to them babies and to that poor man ... and before that in our own house ... " Her voice trailed off. "But the master and mistress aren't going to want to talk about this. And if they know it's come from me, then I really could be in trouble."

She looked at him, straight into his eyes.

"You have to promise me you'll do what you can to protect me."

"I promise," he said.

She sighed. And began to talk.

⋐⊙⊙⊛⊙⊙⊛

The journalist sent a telegram to the editor of the *Freeman's Journal.*

*Scoop. Have picture. She is talking. Waiting on family to agree to interview too.*

After the post office he walked to a pleasant-looking bar in the centre of the town, where he ordered a pint of stout and began to write up the copy in his notebook. He always got a feeling, in his gut, when he was about to uncover something big.

He chuckled as he thought of the *Irish Times* coverage, their articles describing the inside of the house, interviewing the man who had found the bodies, the eerie chill of the room where James Martin had slept, where his babies had been born, where he had likely perished, his body contorted, suffocating, poisoned.

Their coverage had added a certain appeal to the case and a flurry of letters to not only the *Times*, but to the *Journal* too.

What sort of Ireland were they living in at all?

Had no one care of the immortal divinity of these precious souls?

It was Eliza's letter that had set his editor's heart racing.

*There was a Maggie who worked here at the house where I am a maidservant. She was a suspicious person and on more than one occasion we caught her interfering with the children's food.*

*One of our babies perished. I always thought she might have had something to do with it. She left in a hurry last year, and she mentioned to me that she had a job lined up with another family. I wonder if they could be the same person?*

A star witness, found and interviewed by them. By him.

He thought of all his front-page articles, which he'd cut out and stuck to the walls in his bare flat. They were yellow now, curling at the edges, the only decoration in the damp room. This one would need to be framed.

The girl, once she got talking, fed him all the details he needed. He'd posed the questions so that the right emotion poured from her.

"What if she does it again?"

*"She must be stopped."*

"Why do you think she did it?"

*"Because she's a cold-blooded killer. An evil, poisonous woman."*

Evil, poisonous woman.

A gorgeous phrase, a description that would stick, now that they had a witness, someone who actually knew her, who could vouch for her true wickedness.

He wrote out the headlines in his notebook.

*Hunt for Silent Killer Continues*

*Wicklow Baby May Also Have Perished at Hands of Cruel Killer*

A tingle ran up his back, a mixture of the gulps of stout and the deliciousness of the story.

As the interview proceeded and he gained her confidence, Eliza had lost her fearfulness.

Yes, she would do all she could to help bring the woman to justice.

If a photograph of herself would help, outside the house where they both worked, she would do it.

And yes, if he really wanted her to bring these shocking revelations to her master and mistress, she would.

She told him to come back the next morning, by which time she would have spoken to them direct. It was the least she could do to have that woman stopped.

His colleagues at the *Times* and *Independent* would be sick with envy. How fortunate that the girl had written to the *Journal* and not them.

*Exclusive.* He wrote the word across the top of his notes and underlined it.

God bless Eliza.

When he left the pub, wobbling a little, he stopped and clutched at a house wall to steady his gait. He looked up the street, his eyes searching for a sign that read *Guest House*.

A large brown dog barked and crossed the road, trotting along beside him as he walked.

He reached down and ruffled the mastiff's ears.

It was the dog from the house, still loose, less fearsome-looking now that they were acquainted.

A dog would be a lovely companion. After this case was over, he'd get a pup.

It'd be less hassle than a wife anyway.

# CHAPTER 36

## *The Nanny*

James Martin was a country man, soft and stupid. Christy had got that tip-off from someone inside, someone who told him about his cousin, a man with twins whose wife had just died, living in a lovely big country house in the Strawberry Beds.

Maggie had turned up at the right time, telling him she was in the area looking for work and she'd heard about his tragic loss and if he liked she could give him a hand, for bed and board, no payment or anything.

He thought she'd fallen out of heaven. When she touched his crotch one night after filling him full of port, he knew she had.

James was a different man to William D. Thomas

though. William was a much more refined man, educated, learned. She'd had to move slower in Drogheda, taking her time, allowing their friendship to grow naturally.

There'd be no groping under the kitchen table after a rake of drink at Number 43, Laurence Street.

She thought about the twins, buried, rotting, undiscovered in that garden, beloved of James. She thought of that man who had bought the house and his family running around, no idea what lay under the earth, hidden in the soil. The thought made her smirk.

That man had surprised her that day, turning up on the doorstep looking to view the house and the twins still upstairs in their cradles. She'd put the sign up only the day before. She hadn't expected any viewers so soon.

She knew by him that he'd buy. She knew by his itching and hovering and clearing his throat as he spoke that he'd never lived in a house like that before and with the sale price she was going to give him, there was no way he could refuse.

Five kids he said he had.

So up she went to the twins, lying there asleep, the medicine she'd been adding to their bottles keeping them asleep most of the time anyway.

She'd been building it up, letting it work its way through them, poisoning them and sedating them at the same time so she wouldn't have to listen to their squalling.

Jesus, she was tired of those babies. They never stopped. Bawling, roaring. In unison. Apart. It had taken all her will to pretend to James that she cared for them.

Twins were always greeted as a miracle. But she saw it as a curse, a double punishment for some sort of sin the parents must have committed in the past. No sooner had you one changed and fed and settled, then the other one would start the other off again. You constantly had one under your arm, bouncing them up and down, shushing.

She didn't bother with the poison, there wasn't time when that man called. Instead she put a bundled blanket over their mouths, holding it there until their tiny struggles stopped and when she took the blanket away there was no breath left at all.

Snuffed out, just like that.

Already there'd been too many nosy neighbours stopping by and asking questions about James and wasn't it strange how he'd gone so quick in the end, and them not getting to see him or know much about it?

That man knocking on the door, looking to buy the house was the signal to get it all done and quickly.

The suitcase was a nice touch, she thought, taking them from the house, completely unseen.

It had taken her a while to dig that big hole. The earth was hard and frosty. She poured a kettle of boiling water over the muckiest patch she could see in Jame's vegetable corner and used the trowel to hack at the soil.

The sweat had run down her temples and wet her nose, stinging her face. But it had worked out well. Once she got under the surface, the clay was softer, James late winter digging a blessing.

And when they were in there, when she'd finally tossed them in and shovelled the clay back down on top and smoothed the whole thing over, she felt satisfied.

James was gone, the twins were gone and if this man was going to buy the house like he probably would, then she would have a good big lump of the money they needed.

The money for her and Christy's future. For their new life.

It was meant to work out like that, that man turning up all ready to buy the house, not even asking any questions or minding about bank accounts. He just couldn't wait to get his hands on the deed. All he saw was him and his kids moving in between those walls, running around the garden, looking out at the countryside.

Christy was happy she was done. He'd been getting impatient with her, saying there was too long of a gap between the death of James and her staying on at the house. She needed to be getting out of there.

But she wasn't sure where she was to go. It wouldn't be long until Christy's release and she was thinking, if she could just sit tight, stay at the Strawberry Beds for a bit longer, then when he got out they could escape together.

Until Christy wrote about another stroke of luck.

The house where his *'whore of a sister'* worked was looking for a nanny.

*The mother died. She's up the walls, says Susan. Notice going in Drogheda Conservative next week. Get yourself to Drogheda, good woman!*

Good woman.

Another man without a wife. Another child without a mother.

A chance to secure justice against the woman who had ruined Christy's life.

And she would visit Kitty again and give her back what was rightfully hers.

It was time to go home.

ॐ

"Is it inappropriate? I can wear something else," she

blustered, touching the diamond earrings. "It's just, they're exquisite. It's such a shame to see them lying up. I thought by giving them an outing again it would be a tribute."

Margaret was dressed in a formal dinner dress, her hair pinned up, Anna's drop diamond earrings glinting in her lobes.

His face had fallen when he'd seen her, dressed for dinner, in the nursery.

He took her hand and kissed it.

"I couldn't think of a more fitting model," he said. "But it's not that, Margaret."

He paused and looked her in the eyes, the smile he'd given her fading.

"I'm afraid you won't be able to come to dinner tonight. Mrs. Winchester has invited guests and I'm pretty sure, from the sound of it, a potential bride for me. I just can't broach the subject of our relationship tonight. I thought I could, but ..."

Her expression dropped.

"William ..."

"I know," he said. "I know. But tonight is not the right time. It's the first time I've been back here in so long. And Anna Genevieve's first proper visit too. I think it was a bit premature of us. I think it wouldn't be fair to Anna's memory."

Margaret bowed her head.

"Keep the earrings. I've been wondering what to do with all her things. I think Anna would be glad that they were being made use of. But please, don't wear them here. Not yet."

"You're ashamed of me."

"I'm not ashamed of you, Margaret!" said William. "But things are a bit delicate. The Winchesters are grieving for their only daughter. We need to take things slowly."

"This isn't what we discussed," she said.

"I know," he said. "But I don't want to go through it with the Winchesters tonight. In the coming weeks, we will arrange something else. Something away from Swinford perhaps."

She was quiet. Sullen.

"I don't wish to do anything to dishonour your wife in any way."

He wrapped his arms around her, his fingers falling to the bustle of her dress. They kissed, until she pulled away, leaving him wanting more.

She could see it in his eyes, feel it against her, in his embrace.

Her soft approach had worked. She had, in so many small ways, become everything that his wife had been: a companion, a confidante and lately, even her image.

She had gone through Anna's things and started to wear them now. Jewellery, blouses, her powders, brooch pins. She studied a picture of Anna, framed on the dressing table in William's room, a picture she knew William stared at every day.

She copied her hair in the photo, curling and pinning her fringe in the exact same fashion.

She bought a watercolour and had it framed, presenting it as another gift to William, mentioning how the painting made her think of a summer's day, that summer's day when they took the river cruise.

That was the day he had fallen in love with her.

In the end, his proposal had been swift, by the fire, after a full bottle of wine.

"If you are agreeable, I would like to propose marriage," he said. "It would all be out in the open then and we could deal with any fallout from any of our peers ... from the Winchesters."

"That would make me most happy, William."

"You would be agreeable?"

"I would."

"Well, then that's settled then. We will organise a quiet wedding, as soon as possible."

He went upstairs and came back with an emerald ring, mounted with two amber stones and surrounded by diamonds. It glinted in the candlelight in a blue velvet box.

"This was Anna's," he said. "You will be able to tell Anna Genevieve as she grows that her mother wore it before you, and now you wear it as a sign of the great love her father felt for her mother. And now, you."

"It's beautiful," she said, drawing in a breath and touching her chest in admiration.

She slipped it on her finger, where it hung, heavy.

It was she who suggested they break the news when they visited Swinford Hall with Anna Genevieve. She said they should tell the Winchesters together. That way, they couldn't talk him out of it.

"You can bring me to dinner, present me. There will be nothing they can say then."

He had agreed, but she'd sensed his nervousness. All the way over in the carriage, she could feel it.

He was too soft.

And now he had gone back on his word. Being here, in their company, listening to their endless questions and statements about their 'darling Anna' and 'bonny Anna Genevieve'. It had affected him. He wasn't brave enough to go through with their plan. He wasn't even brave enough to stop Mrs. Winchester speaking down to her, like a lowly servant.

With William's arms wrapped around her back, she buried her head into his collarbone and sighed. She couldn't wait to be with Christy again. To feel his touch.

She looked forward to her life ahead with him. Whatever it would be, wherever it would be. Maybe not even in this country, maybe America called them.

She'd put that in her next letter ... *Christy I've been thinking of America, what say you?*

She hoped he'd say yes. She was tiring of Ireland with its grey streets and its gossipmongers and interwoven families all bearing down. In America she'd arrive as a lady. There'd be no workhouse past, no whore of a mother, no lowly nanny status for her.

Lady Margaret.

She felt Christy was near. She could feel it, low, in her stomach.

He was coming.

∽⊙∾

She took the solution and measured out the drops. One, two, three. She watched it curl into the milk on the spoon and disappear. No trace. She tipped the spoon into the Anna Genevieve's bottle and put the teat back on and shook it.

Then she looked at the baby in the cot, the same cot her mother had once lain in.

From a pocket, secretly sewn into her case, she removed the green box of rat poison.

The packaging sent her pulse raising. Goose bumps prickled her skin.

She'd show them.

They didn't deserve to have a lovely evening, fa-faaing around the table. A bride for William? Who did they think they were, matching him up like that? And why didn't he stand up for her?

All those sweet nothings and still he couldn't present her, like they had agreed.

He was a coward.

She took the teat off the milk bottle again and tipped a tiny amount of the poison power into the milk.

Their dinner would be ruined. They'd probably call the doctor.

She took the baby from her cot and nursed her, humming an old Irish air, watching as the baby suckled on the teat, the milk bubbling, flowing into her mouth.

Soon she would be arching her back, her stomach a knot, her bowels caught up.

She thought of how small the organs were, inside, how they'd fight the poison, doing their best to rid themselves of it, her towellings an explosion, the horrible stink a sign of the duress her little body was under.

William would be devastated.

But that was how it worked. If he had treated her better, taken her to dinner as they'd planned, let her dress up and present herself like the lady she was – if he had taken on the Winchesters, told them of their engagement, faced up to the situation like a man – well, then, she wouldn't have had to punish his baby.

She'd been good to William, keeping the child quiet for months now, giving her just the right amount of medicine every day to keep her sedated, to let her sleep most of the time.

Tonight, that would change.

Tonight, he would be taught a lesson.

# CHAPTER 37

## *The Finding of the Clue*

"How would you describe her cheekbones? Were they set high or was there more fat to her face?"

The man was feeling quite fed up now. The fatigue of the past few weeks had finally caught up on him. He was tired from work, from the long journey in and out of the city, from the barrage of questions and conversations about the whole blasted thing. Still they kept coming.

The artist opened a large sketchpad and flicked rapidly through a range of faces, already drawn on the pages.

"Were they like this, or more like this?"

It was hard to remember the woman if truth be told.

He hadn't spent that much time in her presence. He had a picture of her in his mind, one that he had gone over, that had formed and settled into a witch-like, hard-faced woman. Fed by press reports. Confirmed by nightmarish dreams.

But he wasn't sure if that was really a picture of her at all. He felt they should be asking someone who knew her better than him. How the damn hell would he know how high her flaming cheekbones were?

"Would you run and get herself next door and ask her to come and see me?" he said to Aidan who was curled in a kitchen chair with a cup and ball. Aidan didn't stop flicking, trying to catch the ball, a frown line across his face.

"Aidan!"

Aidan hopped up.

"Yes, Da?"

"Go and get Mrs. D'Arcy next door. Tell her I need a favour."

"All right, Da."

The man picked up the sketchbook the artist was holding and started to flick through all the faces himself. Never before had he paid attention to people's features like this. Low-set eyes, far-apart eyebrows, bridges across noses that were flat, wide and lined.

Mrs. D'Arcy would be able to help with this. She'd have a knack for this sort of thing, and she'd be only too willing to have a chance to play her part. To tell everyone she'd *practically drawn the sketch herself*.

He sighed.

"Would you like a cup of tea?" he said to the artist. "I think I could do with a break."

"That'd be fine," said the artist and he leaned back in his chair, reaching for his case to remove a pencil sharpener. "I know it's difficult. But we are nearly there. The last few details are what matters."

"That's why I've sent for herself next door. She seems to have a memory for that sort of thing."

The man called his daughter to make the tea. His wife was lying down upstairs, also exhausted from the week's tribulations.

So far, there had been no update on the case, no leads on the woman's whereabouts.

There had, however, been reams of coverage, with more reporters knocking on their door since the coroner's verdict yesterday.

He got up and stood tapping his foot, waiting for the kettle to boil, watching the girl go about setting out some biscuits on a plate and cutting some bread.

"Are you busy?" he asked the artist, trying to make conversation.

"Fairly busy. A lot of court work. Actually, I think I've a sketch in today's."

He took a folded copy of the *Freeman's Journal* from his case and opened it out onto the table, turning the pages, scanning for his work.

"There you are," he said. "He got life imprisonment. Not a very nice case."

The man walked across the kitchen to look.

"You must live in the courts?" he asked.

"I do seem to spend a disproportionate amount of time there," he said. "Wasn't quite how I imagined my future when I was at art school."

Art school. Imagine going to school to study art. Good Jaysus.

He looked at the picture the sketcher pointed out to him and admired it. The drawing was of an angry-looking man, hunched in the dock. He read the article quickly, about the judge's summing up of the case and how long the jury had taken to deliver their verdict.

When he was finished, his eyes wandered to the opposite page, to a photograph of an accident where a horse and carriage had been swallowed into a large hole in the street. Onlookers crowded round, trying to assist the passengers trapped in the red brougham carriage.

He considered the poor horse whose eyes were white with fright.

"My God, did you see the accident in Drogheda?" he said to the artist.

"Yes, shocking, isn't it?"

"Imagine being in there," he said. "Driving along, then next thing you've fallen into a tunnel in the road, huh?"

He read the article, placing it on the table in front of him. He leaned forward.

He brought the paper closer to him, then back again, letting his eyes adjust.

He put the paper on the table and leaned over it, examining it again.

Aidan came in through the back door, with Mrs. D'Arcy shouting a "*Hell-ooo!*".

"Mrs. D'Arcy," said the man, taking a moment to tear his eyes from the page. "C'mere, tell me, look."

He stabbed the photograph with his forefinger, his fingertip landing on a woman's head in the crowd, straining to peer at the tumbled-down horse and carriage.

"Who does that remind you of, who does it look like?"

Mrs. D'Arcy inspected the photograph.

"I'm not sure," she said. "My eyesight isn't the best these days ... but I suppose ..."

She paused. Then looked at him.

"It's not ... is it?"

Her eyebrows arched in shock.

"Is it?" she asked.

"I think it is."

"*Aidan! C'mere!*" shouted the man at his son who was already back in his chair, tossing his cup and ball.

The boy jumped up and came over to the table to look at the photograph his father and Mrs. D'Arcy were staring at.

"Who's that?" asked the man.

"It's the woman who sold us the house," said the boy.

The man turned to the artist.

"There's her bloody cheekbones now."

# CHAPTER 38

*William D. Thomas*

He paced the marble floor, waiting for the sound of the doctor at the door. Upstairs the wails were coming, fast. The child gasped for air, the only break in between her screams. He went to the hallstand, an ornate piece of furniture with a carved mahogany mirror and leaned on it with both hands. He looked into the mirror and saw there were tears in his eyes.

Anna Genevieve had been crying continuously for almost three hours now. She had exhausted herself at one point and passed out, her short breaths giving them all a sense of relief.

But when she started again, jolting, her body arching as though her insides were twisting, a dark foreboding came over him.

It was the same feeling he got the night she was born.

That something big and tragic and crushing was about to happen.

He was going to lose her.

William closed his eyes, letting the tears blink from his lids, and said a quiet prayer.

*Anna. Don't take her from me. Please. Let her live. Is this because of the Nanny? I am sorry. I am truly sorry. Please don't take her from me. She's all I have left.*

☙◦❧

They had all stood in the nursery, Mrs. Winchester, Margaret, and William.

The child had a terrible stomach upset, her towellings rotten, her eyelids swollen.

Flustered, Margaret had given her what they'd brought with them, soothing syrup to help her sleep, but it was having little effect. She had asked for eggs, milk and sugar to be mixed in a bowl and a drop of whiskey added. This she spooned into the baby's mouth, but it all came back up again quickly.

The Hamiltons were seated, practically abandoned, in the dining room, listening to the sharp sighs of Mr. Winchester. Mrs. Winchester was embarrassed at this dreadful breach of courtesy, but could not tear herself away from the sick room.

Margaret was red-faced, the first time William had seen her so out of control.

Babies got sick. They got fevers. They threw up their milk.

But this was something else.

The child was suffering terribly.

"She needs a doctor, William, you must call one," Margaret said.

And so he was called and they waited.

⟡

After William went downstairs to wait for the doctor, mostly because he was finding Anna Genevieve's cries unbearable, Mrs. Winchester turned to the Nanny.

"Did you prepare the bottle differently?" she said. "Could it be the milk making her sick?"

"It is not, ma'am. I prepared it as I always do. Carefully."

"Perhaps the travelling today made her ill."

"Perhaps."

The baby whimpered in her cot, her cries quietening for a moment.

"Miss Murphy, I must speak you on a certain matter. I realise that you are very stressed and it is very worrying to see little Anna Genevieve so ill. But you really must remember your place. You addressed Mr. Thomas as 'William' earlier. Please remember yourself."

The Nanny raised her eyes in a glare. Her nostrils flared.

She folded her arms and said in a low voice: "He asked me to call him William."

"He asked you? You must be mistaken. He's been very upset over the past weeks. Some of his behaviour has probably been odd. Please refer to him as Mr. Thomas, as is right and proper."

"I will call him by whatever name I please."

"I beg your pardon?"

The atmosphere was thick, set with worry over the child, enflamed now by the insolence from the Nanny.

315

"I said I will call him by whatever name I please. We are engaged, and that is my right."

Mrs. Winchester was silent. Then she laughed.

"Engaged? Who do you think you are? Such notions. I've a good mind, Miss Murphy, to see to it that you are dismissed. Immediately."

"Go ahead," she replied. "I was supposed to be coming here on William's arm, but he wasn't brave enough to present me. I *am* William's fiancée. Why do you think I am wearing this?"

She thrust her hand forward, showing the emerald ring on her wedding finger.

Mrs. Winchester gasped. "That was Anna's! You thieving, conniving wretch! Take it off at once! How dare you?"

It was the Nanny's turn to laugh.

The baby began to cry again, starting in a whimper, changing to a moan, then rising to an ear-piercing scream.

The door opened and the doctor walked in, carrying his black bag, a rushing air about him, William hurrying in his wake.

"Right then," the doctor said. "Let's take a look."

He asked for the child's clothes to be removed. The Nanny moved forward to assist.

"William," said Mrs. Winchester. "May I have a word?"

"In a minute," he replied. "I must see what the doctor has to say."

"It will only take a minute," she said. "Please, come with me to the hall."

Frowning, he followed Mrs. Winchester outside. She took him some paces up the corridor.

"The Nanny has just told me some rather alarming

news. That you are to be married? Is she hallucinating?" Her face was a mask of puzzlement.

William sighed and his shoulders shrank.

"No. We are to be married."

"Is this a joke?"

"It is not a joke."

"You are marrying your nanny?"

Her voice was incredulous.

"Her name is Margaret."

"She is not a fit mother for that child," she said, her voice lowered. "How dare you! How dare you do that to my granddaughter. She will be a laughing-stock."

"This is not the time for this discussion," he said. "Anna Genevieve is sick. We can discuss this later. But I will not have you talk ill of Margaret. She has been a wonderful mother to Anna Genevieve."

He turned and walked away from Mrs. Winchester, striding quickly down the corridor.

"*The grief had gone to your head!*" she shouted after him.

In the nursery the doctor looked a little alarmed.

"She is a very ill baby," he said. "I suspect severe gastroenteritis, but I am worried it may be cholera."

"Cholera!" William cried.

"Those formula bottles," said Mrs. Winchester from behind him. "I told you should have got a wet nurse."

"*Would you shut up?*" said William and Mrs. Winchester recoiled.

The doctor laid out two small brown bottles.

"She needs to be kept hydrated. And these should help stop the vomiting and diarrhoea."

"You must all wash your hands, the nursery should be thoroughly scoured. Boil every drop of water that passes her lips. I would advise emptying the cisterns and ensuring the coverings fit tightly."

"But nobody else has been ill, doctor," said Mrs. Winchester defensively.

"The baby is young," said the doctor. "And susceptible. I would advise all new bottles. If you can't find anything suitable until tomorrow, ensure all the teats are turned out and thoroughly sterilised."

The doctor stayed for an hour and they managed to get some fluids into the baby. Mrs. Winchester summoned the housekeeper to have her disinfect the nursery.

Anna Genevieve quietened and fell into a restless sleep, turning her head, her body shuddering at intervals.

If she made it through the night, she had a chance.

Exhausted, the Nanny stayed with the baby, resting her head against the bars of the cot, watching her sleep.

Mrs. Winchester returned downstairs and when William was satisfied that his daughter was more comfortable, he turned to Margaret.

"Why did you tell her? Tonight, of all nights?"

"What are you ashamed of, William?" she asked, her voice muffled against the bars of the cot.

"I am not ashamed of anything. Not one thing. But tonight, of all nights! I don't understand your timing."

"If the water is contaminated here, we should leave in the morning," she said.

He sighed.

"You are right," he said. "If the baby is well enough in the morning, we will return home. I am going to show my face downstairs and I will be back to check on her. Try to get some rest yourself."

He closed the door behind him and walked down the long corridor, dark mahogany doors leading off to the many bedrooms.

He remembered staying here when he was courting Anna. He remembered how they were laid out in their beds, rooms apart, thinking about their whole life ahead of them, longing for their marriage when they could lie together, as one.

Maybe it was a mistake falling for the Nanny. Tonight was a warning sign, from Anna.

Agitated, he went downstairs where the guests had retired to the grand room. He sat in an armchair while a large glass of red wine was poured for him and he took it to his mouth and gulped it, feeling the liquid burn his gullet.

"Something stronger," he said to the butler. "A double, please."

Miss Hamilton, her face soft and white, smiled at him. He looked past her, over her shoulder to where Mrs. Winchester was seated, glaring, her face creased in a frown, her disappointment in him raw.

# CHAPTER 39

## Mrs. McHugh

Her stomach was full of nerves, butterflies that fluttered, making her feel positively sick.

She'd got the early morning train into Drogheda. She'd rehearsed what she wanted to say, the way she wanted it to come out. To warn Mr. Thomas that the Nanny was not all she seemed to be, that she had strong suspicions the child was at risk. She thought of words she could use, to explain about her brother, about how he was a criminal, about how he'd sent the Nanny to get revenge on her.

For putting her brother in prison.

For taking him off the streets.

Along the quays, the moored sailing ships were being

loaded with goods, men shouting and lifting, readying for sail. It was a beautiful morning, calm, the heat of the day getting ready to shimmer on the horizon.

She thought of Mick and the many mornings he had made his way along the quays with his tin lunch box and flask of tea. How she wished she could spot him now, his big shoulders moving, sauntering along by the river, waving to his co-workers, whistling.

When she got to the offices of *Thomas Brothers Shipping Company Ltd* she took a deep breath and opened the door.

Two clerks looked up as she came into the well-lit office.

"Is Mr. Thomas in?" she asked, scanning for her former employer.

One of the clerks shook his head. "No, ma'am. He is not."

"Oh," she said, disappointed.

She had been ready for a battle of sorts, a confrontation, an argument.

"Will he be in soon?"

"Not today, ma'am," said the clerk, a little unhelpfully.

She thanked the clerks and left, finding herself outside in the light, blinking.

There was nothing for it but to make her way to Number 43.

She walked slowly, the butterflies leaping now, and she had to stop for a moment as the nerves took hold.

She hoped against hope it wouldn't be the Nanny who answered the door.

Walking up the narrow alleyway that led as a shortcut to Laurence Street, she came out onto the road, the front of Betty's pub looming in front of her. She blessed herself.

*Betty, look over me now, won't you?*

At Number 43 she drew the knocker back, holding her breath as she rat-tat-tatted on the door she had cleaned and polished what must have been a thousand times over the years.

Ethel.

Thank the Lord. Lovely little Ethel.

"Ethel! How are you?"

"Hello," she replied, a smile breaking out when she saw her. Then, as if remembering, the smile fell and her mouth went sullen.

"I need to speak with Mr. Thomas – is he here?"

"He's not here," said Ethel. "He's gone to Swinford."

"Swinford?" Blast it anyway. "Is she gone with him, the Nanny?"

"Yes," said Ethel.

"When are they due to return?"

"In two days' time, Mrs. McHugh. Is there anything I can help you with?"

Her voice was haughty, not like the kindly Ethel she knew.

"No. I'll come back when they're back then."

"All right," said Ethel and she closed the door.

She walked away from Number 43, her heart dancing out a rhythm in her chest. Two whole days now before she could talk to Mr. Thomas. What if the child was in danger?

Should she try to make her way out to Swinford Hall? But what if they wouldn't let her in? A thief on their property?

Her head was light. In the grocer's on George's Street she stopped to buy a loaf of bread, something that might ease the queasiness in her stomach.

She picked up a newspaper too. It would be something

to distract her, something to take her mind off things while she thought about what she might do.

She handed over her coins to the grocer, then folded the paper into her basket. A headline near the masthead caught her eye. She took it back out and shook it.

She looked at the grocer and he nodded in companionable agreement.

"Is this true?" she said.

"Can you believe it?" he asked.

## SILENT KILLER TRACED TO DROGHEDA
### *Evil Poisoner May Be Living in Louth Town*

A large sketch of a woman graced the front page, her eyes clear, her eyebrows lowered, a blank, staring expression on her face.

"Do you know who she might be?" said the grocer. "The whole town is on the lookout."

Mrs. McHugh put a hand on the counter, to steady herself as a wave of nausea swept through her.

Her basket tipped over, the wrapped bacon falling out onto the newspaper, flattening itself and threatening to wet a patch of the exclusive eight-page supplement.

"It's the Nanny at Number 43," she said, her voice a whisper, before she too unfurled onto the floor.

# CHAPTER 40

## *Christy*

**THE SILENT KILLER,** the headline said.

He read the details, taking in everything that they knew.

There was no mention of him.

He'd picked up the paper on the way to the stables, something he did every morning. He would read it on the rank, in between waiting for fares.

He'd been following the case of the unearthed babies with interest, hoping they would draw a blank and drop their investigation. The last thing he expected to see was Margaret's face staring back at him in an exclusive special supplement.

Damn and blast her anyway.

He thought about what to do. He could send a telegram, arrange a meeting point, plan their escape.

But he didn't want anyone in the post office knowing what he needed to tell her. He didn't want to divulge her name, her address, having to spell it out.

No, he'd have to go to her. There might still be time. The paper would have to circulate, people would need to talk, to summon the police.

If he went now, he might catch her. They could skip it then.

Gather up everything they needed and get out.

Bloody Margaret.

She should have been more careful.

What the hell was she doing burying those babies in the garden where they could be so easily dug up? She'd told him they were well hidden, no chance of being found. And standing around gawping having her photo taken?

They had all the evidence to work with now. Witnesses. Chemical analysis. Had he taught her nothing?

There was no time to go back to his flat to pack up his belongings. He ignored the pale-faced prostitutes sitting on the steps of buildings, some calling to him as he passed. The morning crew.

He was in a bad mood now.

They would miss him today on the rank.

At Amiens Street train station, his cap pulled low, he thought about the journey back to his hometown. The first time in ten years. He hoped to God he didn't meet anyone he knew.

He sneaked onto the train without buying a ticket, going past the conductor with his hand out, who was occupied with a lone woman asking directions to Sydney Parade.

326

He got a seat and hunched up his legs towards the window, pulling his cap over his eyes. He feigned sleep and spread himself out, to put anyone off thinking about sitting beside him.

The train was quiet enough, only a few early day trippers climbing aboard to make their stops along the coast. Malahide. Donabate.

The backs of buildings rushed past, grey houses, windowed up high, bricks revealed, plaster cracked from walls.

Once the city had passed, the commercial buildings turned into neat rows of terraced houses, then spaced out into larger, green gardens, before the coast appeared.

He looked out at the sea, calm and ebbing. It sparkled under the morning sun, stretching out over the horizon, white scraps of clouds separating it from the sky.

He tapped ash from his cigarette onto the small table in front of him, watching the smoke curl past his head, and out the window of the carriage.

His hangover had set in good and proper now.

His stomach lurched a bit when he saw the sign for Drogheda and he stood to get behind a family getting ready to dismount.

Home.

He pulled his neckerchief over his mouth and walked down the Dublin Road, his hands in his pockets, his head down.

The town was just coming to life, shoppers out with baskets, a horde of signs advertising tea and Fry's Cocoa on the side of the hotel at the corner of the quays.

He crossed the bridge and walked up Shop Street quickly, turning into Laurence Street, looking at the numbers of the town houses.

He wasn't quite sure which was Number 43.

When he reached the pale-blue house, he rang the doorbell and rapped on the knocker, confidently.

A young maid answered it.

"Sorry to disturb, love," he said, pulling the neckerchief down a bit from his mouth. "Would the nanny be in today? I need to have a word with her?"

"Miss Murphy?" asked the girl, looking him up and down.

"Yes."

"She's not available today," she said primly.

"Oh," said the man. "It's very important I see her. Are you sure she's not available? I can come in and wait."

"She's not here," said the girl. "She's gone away for a few days, to Swinford Hall."

She stepped forward and straightened to her full height.

"When will she be back?" he asked.

"I think in two days' time, sir."

"All right," he said. "Thanks."

The maid closed the door.

Damn it anyway. He hadn't expected her to be out to the country like that. Although out there, she might be less likely to be spotted.

He didn't know what to do with himself. He'd planned on seeing her straight off, whisking her away, making their escape.

Now she wouldn't be back for two whole days.

He wondered if he should try to make his way out to Swinford Hall. He didn't have the funds to charter a carriage. He could try hitch a lift either, but he had little idea of how far it was.

His head ached, pounding with the remnants of last night's stout and whiskey. He'd woken up in the Monto, to the slaps and pinches of the girl. She'd called her madame in the end to get rid of him and one of the pimps gave him a good boot on the arse when he finally managed to get himself out of the bed, down the stairs and out onto the street.

Whiskey. He had an awful goo on him for whiskey now.

He crossed the road and bought a naggin of Power's from the grocer's. It felt heavy in his hands as he carried it, the neckerchief back at his mouth, head down, walking all the way up the hill, past the workhouse to the old cottage.

Maggie had written that it was unoccupied. He knew by her that she had a hope that they might even move back there, the two of them.

He would have a drink and think about what to do next.

On the way past the workhouse, he stopped at the wall and found the stones he had once chipped out. He pushed them so that they fell into the grass on the other side, just because he could.

# CHAPTER 41

*The Arrest*

A hare leapt from a shallow ditch underneath the rolling wheels of the carriage. A loud knock sounded, the rim of the wheel clashing with the thick thighbone of the animal.

Stunned, it tried to run away, but with its leg broken it could only stagger to the side of the road and drop. It lay down, its chest rising and falling rapidly until the pain and the shock overcame it and its breathing slowed.

Inside the carriage that knocked the hare, sat William D. Thomas, his child and the Nanny. The baby was sleeping in the Nanny's arms, exhausted from illness.

She had made it through the night.

Margaret kept her head in the air, her body turned from him. She was upset.

William too felt aggrieved. He turned from her in the opposite direction, his legs hunched to the side of the carriage, his boots tapping in agitation as they mounted a bump in the road.

"I want a whole new set of bottles when we get home," he said. "Brand new. And we will get new teats, change them weekly."

"Of course," she said.

The carriage passed a milestone indicating four miles to Drogheda.

They would both be relieved to climb out at Laurence Street, shake out their weary travelled limbs and rest.

William wished that Mrs. McHugh was there to greet them. She would have hot water ready, food … comfort.

The sound of a horse galloping by echoed through the carriage. It was followed by another and then another.

William pulled the blind from the window and looked out, but there was nothing to be seen.

When the road narrowed two miles outside Drogheda, their horse slowed, as though sensing something in the air.

The driver slapped the reins, but the horse did not quicken its pace. They rounded the corner, the river white and sparkling in the early afternoon light.

Up ahead, policemen stood round a cordon. A barrier had been erected.

When the carriage slowed to a near halt, William put his head out the window.

"A check point," he said.

The Nanny bristled.

They listened to the driver upfront answer the policeman's questions.

"From Swinford Hall, sir, County Meath."

"Two occupants, sir, and a baby. Mr. William D. Thomas and his nanny."

They heard footsteps on the road. Light broke into the cab as the door was opened. The carriage shook. The baby whimpered.

The policeman looked at the Nanny, who had drawn an arm up to shield herself.

He withdrew his head but kept his hand on the door.

They heard murmuring from outside.

The policeman put his head back into the carriage and looked again at the Nanny.

"Margaret Martin?"

She shook her head.

"What is the meaning of this?" said William.

"Could I ask both of you to dismount, please?"

Overhead swallows dipped and dived, shooting through the air, catching midges and minute flies.

A pigeon flew by. Fat and slow.

William shook his head and looked at Margaret.

She looked back at him defensively.

"We have quite an ill baby on board, I'd really rather not," said William.

"Sir, I kindly ask you both to get out of the cab."

Sighing, William got up and dismounted, reaching back into the carriage to help Margaret with the baby down the rickety steps.

"Sir, could I please ask you to hold the child?" said the policeman.

Margaret brought the baby up to her face and snuggled it. She took a deep breath, smelling Anna Genevieve, before handing her to a protesting William.

The policeman held up a newspaper with a pencil sketch of a brooding woman.

# WANTED FOR MURDER
## *A History of Poisoning Babies*

William snatched the paper from his hand as another policeman took Margaret by the elbow and led her to a black police vehicle parked on the other side of the barrier.

Margaret did not look back. She did not talk or try to wave. She stared ahead, holding her jaw and chin up as the vehicle readied itself to move off.

As they made around the bend in the road, two swallows chased them, swooping and diving, in pursuit of the flies that hovered out of their way.

⚬⊙⚬

Christy woke with a headache that sliced his head in two. He put his palm to his forehead, sitting up from the settle bench he was strewn across. The bench was still here, a large crack in the middle and filled with dust. The place was a ruin though, the cupboards gone, the grate long cold and covered in soot that had fallen over the years from the chimney.

His hand did nothing to ease the throbbing in his brain.

He needed water, but there was nothing wet in sight, except a small drop of Power's Whiskey, settled in the bottom of the glass bottle at his feet.

He lifted it and drank it, straight, the burn cutting his throat, his stomach protesting at another swill of alcohol to be absorbed.

He felt as though he would vomit and he retched but managed to hold in his guts. He got up, feeling the vessels in his head expand with the movement and went to the corner of the room, nearest the door.

334

He opened his trousers and urinated against the cottage wall, spraying it, away from his feet, leaning against the plaster for support.

From outside, the afternoon sun was casting dappled shadows through caked panes of glass.

He needed something to settle his stomach.

Outside, he started down the laneway but the jolt of his steps caused him to pause and retch. He spat out some bile, in the hope that it would make him feel better.

It didn't.

At the top of the hill, nestled above the hundred steps that would bring him back down into the town, Sampson's tavern had a sign advertising bread bowls. Soup and a pint, it would set him right so it would.

A middle-aged cleanshaven man was wiping a glass when he came in and served up the pint of stout with good humour.

"You look like you could do with that!"

Christy said nothing, but grimaced, picked a seat at the furthest, quietest end of the bar and took a gulp. After another few slurps, the pain in his head dulled a little.

"Hair of the dog," he said to the barman and they shared a knowing smile.

The bar was busy with men stopping in on their lunchtime, covered in dust, paint and soot, smelling of dried sweat, crisp chemical tangs mixing with their fresh cigarette smoke.

He wanted to lay his head down on his hands as he waited for his food, such was his weariness. After avoiding her for months, now he needed to see Maggie urgently.

She had the paperwork they needed for their fortune.

All the details on the bonds and accounts where everything was held.

He closed his eyes, listening to the sounds of the bar around him, wondering how he could get to Maggie before everyone else did.

*"Can you believe it? Right here in the town – did ya ever hear the like?"*

*"And she was working here?"*

*"Aye, as a nanny! Good Jaysus. I tell ya, that Thomas fella had a lucky escape. They think she might have been slowly poisoning him and the child. All to get the house. Wicked bitch."*

Christy leaned forward and took another drink of his pint.

*"How long was she here?"*

*"Oh, I don't know, a few months they think. Imagine, her walking by us on the street, all this time, and us none the wiser."*

*"The world is a mad place altogether."*

*"Oh, it is. Shocking so it is."*

He put his palm to his forehead again.

When the bowl arrived, murky carrots steaming in the middle of the bread, he let the smell enter his nostrils.

He drained his pint with his chin in the air, feeling the liquid rush and settle in his stomach. He slammed the pint glass on the table and took a coin from his pocket and threw it on the counter, landing beside the untouched bread bowl.

Outside the smell of honeysuckle from bushes that hung low and wavered at the top of the hill met the stale gush of air from the tavern.

He kept his hands in his pockets, his neckerchief pulled high and walked up the Dublin Road, slowly, purposefully, towards the train station.

It was too late.

Their chance was gone.

Damn Maggie to hell anyway, he always knew she was trouble.

On the platform he pulled out a cigarette and lit it, watching the smoke curl upwards and evaporate in the yellow ironworks ceiling overhead.

"Goodbye, Maggie," he said out loud, as the train pulled in, puffing white steam all along the platform. He picked a window seat, stretching his legs out and lifting them across the seat opposite. If anyone asked him to move, he'd take them by the neck and tell them what to do with themselves.

He would take a steamer from Kingstown, out across the Irish sea. You wouldn't know who was watching the port at Drogheda.

He was in the mood for an adventure.

And he never liked this town anyway.

# CHAPTER 42

*The Nanny*

Her cell was cold and damp. She sat in it alone, shivering under the thin, sack-like blanket. Outside she could hear noise, voices, clanging, the sound of keys.

It reminded her of the workhouse.

Christy had warned her to be careful, and she was. She was discreet about her business, taking care not to make mistakes. It was why she'd sent Ethel up to get the poison for Mick McHugh. No trace back to her. It was why she was careful taking Mrs. McHugh's key to get into the cottage that day. Just for an hour. She put it straight back – the woman had never noticed.

And the handwriting forgery, Mrs. McHugh's letter, getting that man Christy knew who could scribe to any writing sample you provided him. She was proud of that move.

She'd found the valuation certificate for the ring in a drawer in Anna Thomas' dressing table. She would tell Christy that when she saw him, that she *had* been careful.

The guard rapped on the cell door with a baton, the sound startling her.

She heard him unlocking the door and she stood up, her heart beating.

Christy? Had Christy come to see her?

"You have a visitor."

Her joy died when she saw who it was.

She folded her arms, sat down and looked the other way as the guard let Mrs. McHugh into the cell and warned, "Five minutes".

He locked the door behind him, rattling the keys.

She refused to look at Mrs McHugh and a silence hung between them, awkward and tense.

"All that stuff in the papers, is it true?"

Mrs. McHugh's voice was shaky, but she held her head high.

The Nanny shrugged. "What papers? I haven't been reading any papers."

"The newspapers. You're all over them. Poisoning babies. Murdering them. How could you?" Her voice shook again.

"Have you heard from Christy?" She was wondering if he'd been reading the papers too.

"Christy?" said Mrs. McHugh. "Did he put you up to this?"

She shrugged again. "If you're talking to him will you tell him to come and see me?"

"I won't be talking to him."

Silence.

"I need to know. I need you to tell me. About Mick?"

No shrug. Instead, the Nanny turned her head and stared at the cell wall.

Mrs. McHugh began to tremble.

"They're going to hang you."

Another shrug.

"What is wrong with you? How could you do that? To little babies? What is wrong with you?"

The Nanny turned her head to look at Mrs. McHugh.

"Babies die every day. Women are beaten and punched, little girls burnt to death, scalded. Every day. What difference does any of it make?"

"*Who do you think you are, taking babies like that? Taking my Mick?*"

Mrs. McHugh stepped forward, the points of her cheeks red, her whole body shaking with rage.

"Who are any of us?" said the Nanny, turning to face the wall again.

Mrs. McHugh banged on the door and the guard came, his keys sounding on the other side.

"If you see Christy, tell him I'm waiting on him. Tell him I'll see him as soon as I'm out."

Mrs. McHugh shook her head in disbelief. As the guard locked the door, she looked at the Nanny framed through the spy hatch, sitting, arms folded, a pleasant look on her face. Always the trace of a smirk.

Outside the police station stood William D. Thomas, a perambulator under his hands, a pale and wide-eyed Anna Genevieve tapping at a rattle that hung from the hood.

"Well, did you ... did she ...?"

Mrs. McHugh nodded her head.

"I'm so sorry."

"I don't want to talk about it," she said, fighting back tears. "Let's go back home and we'll talk about it again. I'm not able for it right now."

They walked up the street, away from the police station where the Nanny was being held until the upcoming assize.

It was a short walk, past children playing in the street, boys kicking a can, girls sitting watching.

They crossed West Street in silence, both thinking about the escape Anna Genevieve had, about Mick and how he had not been so lucky.

"This is my fault," said William. "If I'd never hired her, none of this would have happened."

"You can't blame yourself. This is on her ... and my brother."

"We will never get over this," said William.

"No," said Mrs. McHugh. "But we will get on with things. For her sake."

She nodded at the baby.

At Laurence Street, Mrs. McHugh took over pushing the pram, Anna Genevieve lying back peacefully against her blankets.

Mr. Thomas walked beside her, his hand on hers where she grasped the handle, squeezing it gently.

They walked like that, hand over hand on the pram, not noticing the heads that turned to watch, or the whispers as they passed, or the fingers that pointed at Mr. Thomas and his bonny baby, his poor housekeeper and her husband not long passed, all the way back to Number 43 Laurence Street.

# CHAPTER 43

*The Aftermath*

A ladybird climbed the wood, slowly, barely moving, red and black on the shiny oak.

The man and woman stood, side by side, looking at the thick-set cross.

"Lovely carving," said the woman.

"He did a fine job."

"And he wouldn't take any money for it?"

"No, said it was a gift, from the parish, to us."

"It's so kind of them."

"Will we say a prayer?"

"Maybe a decade?"

The man began, leading the opening part of the prayer, the woman finishing in hurried, mumbled tones. They prayed over the cross, their backs to the house, where their children looked out the window at their parents who had gone to see what the carpenter had done in the garden.

When they had finished, they bowed their heads and walked back through their garden, past the sunken beds where the potatoes should have been flourishing and ready for harvesting about now.

When they got inside, the woman went to her son and took him in her arms.

Outside a sudden gust of wind moved the ladybird and threatened to upend it and send it tumbling into the soil.

But it stopped, waited and held fast and when the wind was gone, it continued moving, gripping the wood, climbing up the cross toward the lavender sky.

*An Invitation*

*You are cordially invited to the launch of*

**FROM MY WINDOW**
A collection of stories and musings
Taken from the Journals of Betty Farley
24 November 1880
Mayoralty House, North Quay, Drogheda
*Refreshments will be served*

Also on the evening the Anna Winchester
Memorial Cup will be launched.
**A charity event in aid of the Dockers' Union of
Drogheda**
*RSVP to 43 Laurence Street*